101 Secrets to Winning Beauty Pageants

I just thought

You might find

this funny

Ryan :)

101 Secrets to Winning Beauty Pageants

Ann-Marie Bivans

Introduction by
Carolyn Sapp, Miss America 1992

A Citadel Press Book
Published by Carol Publishing Group

A Citadel Press Book
Published by Carol Publishing Group
Citadel Press in a registered trademark of Carol Communications, Inc.
Editorial Offices: 600 Madison Avenue, New York, N.Y. 10022
Sales and Distribution Offices: 120 Enterprise Avenue, Secaucus, N.J. 07094
In Canada: Canadian Manda Group, One Atlantic Avenue, Suite 105, Toronto, Ontario M6K 3E7
Queries regarding rights and permissions should be addressed to
Carol Publishing Group, 600 Madison Avenue, New York, N.Y. 10022

Carol Publishing Group books are available at special discounts for
bulk purchases, sales promotion, fund-raising, or educational
purposes. Special editions can be created to specifications. For
details, contact: Special Sales Department, Carol Publishing
Group, 120 Enterprise Avenue, Secaucus, N.J. 07094

Manufactured in the United States of America
10 9 8 7 6 5 4 3 2 1

Library of Congress Cataloging-in-Publication Data
Bivans, Ann-Marie.
101 secrets to winning beauty pageants / by Ann-Marie Bivans ;
introduction by Carolyn Sapp.
p.   cm.
"A Citadel Press book."
ISBN 0-8065-1643-7 (pbk.)
1. Beauty contests. I. Title. II. Title: One Hundred one
secrets to winning beauty pageants.   III. Title: One Hundred and one
secrets to winning beauty pageants.
HQ1219.B58   1995
791.6—dc20   94-42195
                                                         CIP

Dedication

*T*o my parents, Paul and Margaret, and to my sons, Christopher and David, for their unfailing encouragement and moral support.

Contents

Contents

Contents

Foreword

Charles Dunn
Publisher, *Pageantry* magazine

I am delighted to offer this introduction to *101 Secrets to Winning Beauty Pageants* and its author, Ann-Marie Bivans. There has been growing excitement and anticipation about the release of her new book as a result of the popularity of *Miss America: In Pursuit of the Crown*, her classic documentary of the history of the Miss America Pageant.

By drawing upon her vast experience with some of the industry's most successful personalities, Ann-Marie has become one of the foremost authorities on what it takes to reach one's goals in pageants. Her tremendous amount of research and candid interviews, combined with her ability to cleverly present contestants' stories have made her "Keys to the Crown" column one of the most informative and enjoyable sources for *Pageantry* readers, both young and old.

The message of her book is that the key to success in pageants, career, or in achieving any goal, is PREPARATION. In almost every success story there is overwhelming evidence that with a great deal of detailed planning and preparation, the goal was reached. Most case studies explain the difference between success and failure by the amount of motivation, time, and effort given to acquire the knowledge necessary to excel in every area of competition. I am constantly told of the endless hours of training and dedication that goes into becoming a pageant winner. There is no other statement that better describes *101 Secrets to Winning Beauty Pageants* than to say, "Success doesn't just happen. It is earned!"

Ann-Marie Bivans's insight and knowledge of competition has been a wonderful contribution, not only to *Pageantry* magazine, but also to the entire pageant industry. As a result of hours of interviews and background information contributed by the leaders in the industry, *101 Secrets* will be the single most comprehensive source on what it takes to be a success in pageants.

Acknowledgments

A note of appreciation to the individuals who so generously shared their time and expertise for the benefit of future contestants: Melissa Aggeles; Warren Alexander of the Miss Teen of America Pageant; Terry Atwood of Terry Atwood Photography; David Bartley of Images Photography by David Bartley; Lee Beaman; Kris Beasley; Jeff Bell; Kenn Berry; Wendy Berry; Steve Bishop of Express Trax; Tina Birkett of the Miss Teen All America Pageant; Janet Ward Black; Regina Blakely; Kim Boyce; Adair Brown; Debbie Brown of Brides & Beauties; Donna Breen of the Cinderella Scholarship Pageant; Debbie Bryant Berge; Sarah Burgess of Express Trax; Gretchen Carlson; Christina Chriscione; Joseph Christiano of Body Redesigning by Joseph Christiano; Tricia Copelin of Custom Creations by Tricia; Dr. Shirley Cothran Barret; Marian Cox; Vernon DeSear; Ada Duckett; Charles Dunn; Robin Elliott-Bear of Robin Elliott; Ltd.; Sarah Evans; Mike Fifrick of Fitness from Fifrick; Kati and Nancy Fish of K.T.'s The Winning Edge; Sandy Frick; Terry Meeuwsen Friedrich; Dr. Sandra Adamson Fry-

Acknowledgments

hofer; Dr. Jeffrey Garner; Annette Gerhart of The Cinderella Shoppe; Richard Guy and Rex Holt of GuyRex Associates; Mary Donnelly Haskell; Sam Haskell of the William Morris Talent Agency; Robert Hedberg of the America's Junior Miss Pageant; Kristin Huffman; Dennison Keller; Zola Keller of Zola Keller, Inc.; Stacy King; Wylie King; Roger Knight; Debra Sue Maffett; Nonnie Maffett; Beverly McGinn of Grandma's Angels; Dorothy Benham McGowan; Dana Metz of the Mrs. America Pageant; Paula Miles of Miss USA/Teen USA; Lori Moore of *'TEEN* magazine's Miss Teenage America Pageant; John Moskal; Kathleen Munson of The Pageant Shop; Cheryl Prewitt Salem of C. P. Annie Productions; Jill St. Pierre; Carolyn Sapp; Jennifer Sauder; Laurel Schaefer; Evelyn Ay Sempier; Christi Taunton; Thomas Tolbert of Legends; Kelly Totten of the Miss Universe Pageant; Dr. Debbye Turner; Gussie Turner; Sharon Turrentine of Shape Up with Sharon; Marilyn Van Derbur; Marjorie Vincent; Maya Walker; Peggy White; Donna Axum Whitworth; Kaye Lani Rae Rafko Wilson; and Robert Zettler.

And a special word of appreciation to Denise O'Sullivan for her many hours of work to make this book its finest.

Introduction

Carolyn Sapp, Miss America 1992

In my search for the Miss America title and scholarship opportunities, my life was changed forever! But it began as a
dream. . . . As a small girl, wearing my mother's high-heels or
working in the corral with cattle, I began a vision for myself:
Could I achieve my dreams? As I matured through life experiences, family, love, and educational goals, my personal dream
became a sharper, clearer picture. A very specific dream of
mine was to help shoulder the responsibility of my education,
to help my parents on a financial level, and gain the self-pride
associated with taking charge of one's educational goals. The
Miss America Scholarship system provided me the perfect vehicle to take charge of my personal educational vision. The
remarkable opportunity presented by the program and its very
fiber is supporting young women's exceptionally personal
search for their dreams.

Each of us across this country and around the world has a
different dream. Dreams are a part of your soul which will
become memories you will cherish. The personal search for

your dream will light your imagination and create your vision for tomorrow. Armed with your dream, your search begins. I assure you it will be a fascinating journey.

Like all travel, there will be many dedicated professionals and volunteers to assist you along the way. Their dedication, energy, and professional attitude will help you gain a broader global perspective of our world, formulate new opinions, and help you make your dreams a reality. As with all things in life, direction and advice from others should be "taken with a grain of salt." Please remember their *intentions* are always good. Nothing will change your life like the people you will meet through pageants. Like jewels, they will bring gladness to your heart. As Miss America, I became a part of history as I looked into the hearts of those people across America.

In the pageant process young women receive a treasure chest of opportunities. In this treasure chest, the greatest jewel is self-discovery—the opportunity to develop your own vision of yourself, what you could become, what you could dream, how you can contribute to the promise of humanity.

A winning positive attitude is an essential part of this process. The best rule of thumb in life is to embrace a positive attitude like your best friend. It has been proven that your ability to see light and goodness in the most difficult situations is simply a matter of a positive attitude. Imagine pursuing the crown as walking down a path filled with irreplaceable opportunities to find yourself.

This book will become an essential part of your quest for the crown. Its table of contents will offer you a plan for preparation. *Preparation* is one of the greatest elements of the pageant process . . . but preparation to pursue the crown must be tailored to your individual perception. That perception will change as you mature in the pageant process. Each stage of competition requires a different approach. I can still remember the joy of my first preliminary pageant held in Kona, Hawaii.

It was as if I went from the sun-drenched seashore to the pageant stage in *one* day! Personal choice defines how seriously *you* approach this life opportunity. Look deep within yourself and define what dream you'll set your sights on. Defining that "right" choice is very simple: The right choice is *your* choice.

A simple mathematical approach may take the weight off your shoulders. First, read this book, cover to cover. This will not only provide many avenues to consider, it will give you a real perspective on the pageant process. In each phase, look carefully at the present scoring system. This will give you an indication of what the pageant is looking for. The secret to success is to understand how those parts make up the whole. Look into each chapter and then combine it all with your inner voice. Second, *understand* yourself—your strengths and the areas you may need to develop. Last, believe in yourself and in your choice. A crown may be only a preliminary pageant away! But know that on a different day, someone else might be crowned. Take the attitude that you did things *right* and made the right choices, rather than questioning yourself to find what you did "wrong."

If you were to walk in my shoes for a moment, it wouldn't be evening gown heels. It would be *interview shoes* you would wear. The benefit of the interview process is the opportunity to develop your style and express what is in your heart. These interview shoes have taken me from my island paradise to the greatest cities across America and around the world. No matter where I walked, I was filled with God's amazing grace and people's genuine smiles.

As a personal commitment to myself and to God, I decided to give my year [of service] 200 percent. I reached out to America and offered dreams with a reality-based platform. What I received in return is almost too great for words. How can one write about love, smiles, embraces, and receiving the joy one feels in their heart? Miss America was more than I ever expected and, even today, I am still moved to excitement and humbled when I think of my personal joy and the friendships I have made.

To each and every one of you, I wish that all your personal dreams come true. Take the hand of a willing pageant volunteer, work hard, have a loving heart, be a genuine friend, and most important—remember God's perfect plan for your life is already in His hands. And the crown will always be yours!

Aloha pumehana

A Message From the Author

Congratulations. By picking up this book you have taken an important step along your road to the crown. Whether you are a new contestant who wants to begin competing on a good footing or a veteran contestant seeking a winning edge to help you capture the crown the next time around, *101 Secrets to Winning Beauty Pageants* will provide you with invaluable strategies for success. This book offers straight talk from the experts in the industry: respected pageant officials and judges, national titleholders and state winners, and nationally recognized authorities in every area of pageant competition preparation.

I consider the advice these experts have shared to be invaluable "keys to the crown." As a contestant you can never predict exactly which "key" will impress the judges and open the door to victory. Maybe the key that earns you the crown will be your charming sense of humor during a stressful national judges interview that intimidates the other contestants. Or perhaps that winning key will be an evening gown which makes you look so stunning that the judges wouldn't dream of bestowing the crown on anyone else. Of course, there is no way to know what might tip the scales in your favor and put the crown within your reach. Yet one fact is certain. When that crucial moment comes and the judges are deciding whether *you* should wear the crown, you want to know every key that might unlock the door to victory. This book is designed to provide you with those keys—advice from experts, strategies for success, and inspiring real-life examples that can give you the winning edge to succeed in your quest for the crown.

Win With Experts' Strategies for Success

Winning will require belief in yourself, knowledge, hard work, and proven strategies for success. Through over fifteen years of research I have enjoyed the privilege of knowing hundreds of state and national judges and titleholders, pageant officials, since-deceased legends of pageantry, and respected pageant trainers, coaches, and consultants. Conversations with these experts and my own exhaustive research have convinced me that Lady Luck doesn't award the crown. Specific behaviors, attitudes, choices, and competitive strategies enable determined young women to navigate the road to the crown successfully. *101 Secrets to Winning Beauty Pageants* will reveal the winning behaviors and strategies that enable a young woman to compete at her best.

Chapter 2, "Your First Steps on the Road to the Crown," will explain how major pageants seek *different* qualities in their titleholders, how you can determine which pageants *you* are most likely to win, and how you can convince judges that you are a winner *before* they ever meet you.

Chapter 3, "The Winning 'Package'," will share the specific qualities you *must* have to be considered for the crown. I will share how visualization techniques can prepare you to win, how you can turn repeated failures into victory, the secrets to handling the press like a pro, and how your voice could cost you the crown.

Chapter 4, "The Winning Interview," explains how what you do *before* the interview is as important as the interview itself, what mistakes could cost you the crown, how to recover when you don't know an answer, and what questions you *must* answer or "flunk" your interview.

In Chapter 5, "The Winning Swimsuit," learn the exercises top fitness trainers recommend for developing a winning figure, and swimsuit designers' trade secrets for camouflaging figure flaws. Discover how a suntan can make you look slimmer, the tricks to making your bustline look two sizes larger, and how you can use "color psychology" to gain higher scores.

Whether you have a great talent—or no talent at all—Chapter 6, "The Winning Talent," will tell you how to create, improve, or fake, a stage talent. Learn the secret to selling *any* talent and how to turn an onstage disaster into extra points. Refer to my exclusive list of the most successful musical selections ever performed in pageants—available to contestants for the first time ever!

Chapter 7, "The Winning Evening Gown," reveals the worst mistakes girls make in their choice of gown, why you should always check your gown under stage lights, how to use color psychology to "tell" judges who you are. Discover the gown colors statistically most likely to win—published for the first time in *101 Secrets.* Take along my handy "Guide to Figure Camouflage" (Tip #85) when shopping for your competition wardrobe.

In Chapter 8, "Winning Onstage Communication," you'll learn how to communicate to win during onstage interviews: how your words create a winning—or losing—image, what to do when you bomb on an answer, and how to clinch the crown with the final question.

And Chapter 9, "Your Final Steps in Pursuit of the Crown," reveals two steps you can take when you've lost and lost and lost.

Go for the Rhinestones

Pageants are an exciting, fulfilling hobby that can pay off with rewards a young woman might never have dreamed possible. Ask Leanza Cornett, who went from an unknown college student, to Miss America 1993, to *Entertainment Tonight* cohost in one year. Since pageants have the ability to transform your life radically, give yourself the advantage of being well prepared to pursue—and win—the rhinestones and roses. Study the secrets to winning and invest the time and effort to develop the qualities that can help you earn that thrilling victory-walk down the runway one day.

The term "beauty pageants," as used in this book's title, is used in the broadest generic sense of the word and in no way is intended to suggest that all pageant competitions included in this book are beauty pageants, per se. The term has been used only because of its universal usage and acceptance by the public and press to describe pageant competitions.

In particular, the author would like to emphasize that the Miss America Pageant, officially titled the Miss America Organization, is the leading personal development/leadership program for women and the largest private women's scholarship program in the world. Other pageant programs discussed in this book, such as America's Junior Miss, Miss T.E.E.N., and Miss Teen of America, also eschew the phrase "beauty pageant."

The author recognizes the efforts of these programs to move away from judging females on physical beauty alone, and applauds their achievements providing invaluable opportunities for females to enrich their lives personally, financially, and professionally.

My hope is that *101 Secrets to Winning Beauty Pageants* will bring you closer to achieving your dreams by providing the keys to your crown. Here's to your success. . . .

101 Secrets to Winning Beauty Pageants

ONE

Why Compete?

*It was a year of
tremendous growth for me.*
GINA TOLLESON, MISS WORLD 1990

You have a dream and you've chosen pageants as a vehicle to achieve that dream. Wise choice. Pageants are in the business of making dreams come true.

Every contestant's dream is different. For some, like Miss Universe 1993, Dayanara Torres, the ambition might be to fulfill a childhood dream of winning a national or world title. Others hope to use the publicity to launch entertainment careers. Even before giving up their Miss America crowns, Carolyn Sapp (1992) starred in the television movie *Miss America: Behind the Crown* and Leanza Cornett (1993) signed a four-year contract with *Entertainment Tonight*. Many, like former Miss Americas, attorney Rebecca King Dreman and Dr. Debbye Turner, pursued the crown to earn scholarship money to finance advanced education. Some want the whole package. Media superstar Diane Sawyer used her victory as America's Junior Miss for 1963 to achieve a coveted dream, finance her education at Wellesley College, work for a president, and launch a stellar career as host of *60 Minutes* and *Prime Time Live*.

Whatever the goal, the quest for the crown always begins as a dream. "I think every little girl dreams about being Miss America," says Kaye Lani Rae Rafko, Miss America 1988. "Everyone I've ever talked to has said that when they were growing up they would watch the pageant. When Miss America was crowned they'd run down the hall and get their silk flowers and pretend to take their runway walk."

Even in an era of feminism, the fantasy of gliding down the runway with the roses continues to tantalize millions of young women. Over 3 million girls enter 750,000 pageants each year in the United States. In South America, beauty contests are a cultural craze, with Colombia alone crowning a new beauty queen every twenty-four hours.

Even the constraints of communism and the ravages of war haven't dimmed the dream. In 1988, when a call was issued for contestants for a Miss Moscow contest, organizers were swamped with over 2,700 responses, and patriotic young women competed before capacity audiences in the Miss Besieged Sarajevo and Miss Lebanon contests.

Stepping Into Cinderella's Glass Slippers

Why are millions of women from around the globe on a quest for the crown? Like a modern-day Cinderella story, a major pageant title instantly lifts a girl-next-door from obscurity into the celebrity spotlight. As actress Eva Gabor, a former national pageant judge observes, "The young lady who wins in a moment will become a celebrity, such as all of us on this judges' panel have worked our whole lives for."

Indeed, when Colombia's Luz Zuluaga brought her country its first Miss Universe crown, the government welcomed her home as royalty, declared a national holiday, and awarded her a mansion and tax-exempt status for life. Not bad for an eighteen-year-old.

Pageants' reputation as a ticket to stardom is strengthened by the big names who launched their careers from a runway. Talk-show superstar Oprah Winfrey first talked her way into the Miss Fire Prevention and Miss Black Tennessee titles. Cybill Shepherd lost Miss Teenage America but moonlighted as "Model of the Year," and Linda Carter traded her Miss World-USA crown for *Wonder Woman's* armor. Halle Berry graduated from Miss Teen All American 1985 to star in Alex Haley's miniseries, *Queen.* Miss USA 1970, Deborah Shelton, romanced "J.R." in *Dallas,* while Laura Herring, Miss USA 1985, married a European count and filmed *Lambada: The Forbidden Dance.*

Miss Americas always fare well. Phyllis George made history as TV's first female sportscaster (*NFL Today*) and married a governor, John Y. Brown, of Kentucky. Mary Ann Mobley and Lee Meriwether won acclaim as actresses. The most famous winner of all, Vanessa Williams, discovered that even dethroned title-holders gain from the fame.

Yet, you don't have to *win* to find your key to stardom. When Sophia Loren entered the Miss Rome contest she caught the eye of film producer Carlo Ponti, a judge. Although she lost the contest, she won Ponti, international fame, and an Oscar. Michelle Pfeiffer missed the Miss California throne, but later reigned in Hollywood, and Sharon Stone lost Miss Pennsylvania but soared to fame in *Basic Instinct.* In fact, scores of celebrities who *lost* the crown used pageant runways to launch their careers: Kim Basinger, Delta Burke, Raquel Welch, Paula Zahn, Vanna White, Deborah Norville, Mary Hart, Morgan Fairchild, Loni Anderson, Susan Anton, Nancy Stafford, Barbara Eden, and Academy-award winner Cloris Leachman.

Seeking Success

With such notable alumnae it's not surprising that pageants maintain an unshakable appeal to girls from Texas to Tokyo. For the ambitious girl-next-door seeking a ticket to success, pageants provide a wealth of opportunities, including:

- millions of dollars in scholarships
- personal income as high as $200,000
- prize packages reaching $250,000
- interview practice and training
- publicity and career contacts
- expense-paid travel, often international
- an entrée into celebrityhood

Pageants are a savvy strategy for girls determined to start life off on a strong footing, as shown by the caliber of women whose stint in pageantry launched their impressive careers. Pageant "graduates" include: Emmy and Academy award winners, MBAs, Ph.D.s, executives, physicians, dentists, psychiatrists, professors, lawyers, as well as a state senator, state supreme court judge, aerospace engineer, Marine officer, minister of tourism, CNN anchor, veterinarian, engineer, state lottery director, FAA director of Federal Legislation, and a Wall Street stockbroker. "Girls don't just want to be [the winner] anymore. It's just a stepping stone along a career path," says Regina Blakely, a former Miss Arkansas who attended law school entirely on pageant scholarships.

Often pageants literally birth new careers. "I didn't know what I wanted to do career-wise," explains former Miss America Debra Maffett, host of *TNN Country News* and creator/host of *Hot, Hip and Country*. "Before [pageants] I would never have dreamed that I could host a national show. It helped me build my confidence and find out what my talents were. It's not that the pageant got those things for me, but I would never have even developed those aspects of myself because I would never have had a safe stage to evolve in those areas. The Miss America program was literally a fertile ground on which I could develop myself." That development whisked her from

Cut 'n Shoot, Texas, to an entertainment career that has included an Emmy nomination, hosting *PM Magazine*, *Alive and Well*, and *Guinness Amazing World Records*, appearing in *Matlock* and *Pass the Ammo*, and recording an album, *Die Trying*. Not bad for a girl who didn't know what she wanted to do in life.

Whether a young woman aspires to knock 'em dead in Hollywood or climb the corporate ladder, pageants can provide the finances and professional contacts to launch almost any career. One Miss America, Kylene Barker (1979), used her contacts and appearance income to open a women's apparel shop, D. Kylene's, on Palm Beach's exclusive Worth Avenue. Another aspiring entrepreneur, Janelle Commissiong, Miss Universe 1977, explained the crown's career value after winning her international title: "It's a business really, and when I got into it I knew it was a business. The thing is to take as much out of a situation as you can. It's up to you to get the most out of the experience."

As the track record proves, pageants are a winning career launch-pad for ambitious young women, whether or not they walk away with the crown. "Even if you don't win that title, the opportunities are phenomenal," explains Kaye Lani Rae Rafko, now a world-renowned speaker.

Largest Source of Women's Scholarships

Contestants also stand to gain a great deal financially. Despite critics' claims that pageants are exploitive, "scholarship pageants" such as the Miss America and America's Junior Miss programs are the largest private source of scholarships in the world for women, offering millions of dollars in scholarships annually. The unquestionable leader, the Miss America Organization, makes available over $24 million in scholarship opportunities each year and a $35,000 scholarship to Miss America. The America's Junior Miss program for high school seniors awards $2 million in scholarships and a $30,000 scholarship to America's Junior Miss. The Miss T.E.E.N. Pageant presents $300,000 in awards, and *'TEEN* magazine awards Miss Teenage America a $15,000 scholarship.

That assistance can determine whether a young woman completes her education. Kaye Lani Rae Rafko competed to earn nursing school tuition. "I came from a middle-class family and we struggled to make ends meet," she says. "I needed financial assistance, but I couldn't rely on scholastic or athletic scholarships. My only choice was the Miss America Pageant unless I wanted to pay back student loans until the year 2000." Competing in the program ultimately earned her over $200,000 in scholarships and appearance income.

"The stakes are high and women know they can gain a lot from [pageants]," says her fellow titleholder Marilyn Van Derbur, who is currently an educational film producer. "When boys are going out for football scholarships, young women are going out for Miss America scholarships and funding their education. . . . I think young women are more educated as to what they can gain from doing it."

Personal Development

Pageants encourage entrants to view their participation as a personal development strategy to help them gain valuable skills and become more successful people.

Although the public thinks of pageants as mere "beauty contests," many are much more than that. Some programs omit swimsuit competitions, require good grades, and emphasize outstanding individuals. "Yes we offer a *tremendous* amount of scholarships to contestants," explains Robert Hedberg, of the America's Junior Miss scholarship program, "but the true value of our program is the personal development and the self-esteem building process. We have a motto: 'A *representative* is selected from a group of *winners*, rather than a winner from a group of representatives.' That really underlines the philosophy of our program."

Similarly, the Miss America Organization, easily the standard-bearer for pageants, defines itself as "the nation's leading achievement program for young women of the 21st century . . . a vehicle for personal achievement and career advancement for the best and brightest of these women."

Underscoring such programs' contributions to women's lives, a study published in *USA Today* linked pageant participation with increased personal development. Dr. Glenn Good compared 155 local titleholders with 229 college students with similar backgrounds. The results revealed that both groups were equal in emotionalism and sensitivity, but the contestants were "more active, ambitious, and independent" than the students who had not competed.

Evidently, by encouraging goal-setting and "stretching," pageants help girls to achieve their potential. "I think anytime a young person has a dream or sets goals to reach for there is growth involved," says Debra Maffett. "With pageants you are trying to develop yourself to your maximum potential. It doesn't matter who wins. The fact that you've gone through the process means that you have grown and bettered yourself. If you're trying to evolve yourself for your goals in life, pageants are a wonderful learning process to help you in that direction."

Career Communication Skills

Pageants also provide girls with an excellent platform to develop the communication skills necessary for their future careers. A titleholder gives press interviews and speeches, debates critics, and converses with people from all walks of life. She learns to think on her feet and to communicate with confidence in challenging situations. "The stage experience and experience dealing with people that I gained as Miss North Carolina is absolutely invaluable to my ability to communicate," asserts attorney Janet Ward Black, a senior law firm partner and former state assistant district attorney. "The interpersonal communication that pageants helped me develop is a valuable tool that I use every day of my life."

Pageants are especially effective for equipping college women to excel in job interviews. By repeatedly undergoing pageant interviews, contestants master the art of "selling" themselves in stressful situations. In a competitive job market that ability is invaluable. "There is no doubt in my mind that I would not have been hired if I didn't have the experience I gained in the pageant," asserts former Miss Arkansas Christi Taunton, a pharmaceutical specialist. "That makes it all worthwhile for me—to know that I used the experience I gained from that year to go on with my life."

Perks, Prizes, and Profit

Another reason contestants participate is the perks, prizes, and profits of the crown.

Prize packages vary according to the region and level of competition. Most local titleholders win gifts donated by sponsors and a modest scholarship, while state winners earn more substantial award packages. Miss Texas's jackpot often includes a computer, fur coat, diamond jewelry, and a $30,000 wardrobe. Some pageants also provide their titleholder with an apartment, car, and gas allowance during her reign.

Appearance income is another attraction. Although local winners often make unpaid appearances to gain experience, state titleholders can earn substantial appearance income, especially in the South where pageants are most popular. For instance, Miss South Carolina makes over five hundred appearances and can bank $80,000 in appearance fees during her reign. Local and state scholarships can add as much as $30,000 to a contestant's earnings.

If the contestant goes on to win a major title, she will enjoy first class travel and accommodations and the services of a business manager and traveling companions. In addition, Miss USA and Miss Universe are provided a luxury apartment to share during their reigns.

National titleholders also earn hefty prize packages. Miss Teen All American wins $5,000 cash, a personal-appearance contract, fur coat, luggage, and other gifts, while Miss Teen of America wins a $40,000 prize/scholarship package. Miss America drives off with a new Corvette, Miss Teen USA wins $150,000 in prizes and cash awards, and Miss USA and Miss Universe each win a prize package valued at $200,000. In addition, Miss USA and Miss Universe win a $40,000 employment contract, Miss Teen USA wins a $30,000 employment contract, and Miss America can expect to earn $150,000 to $200,000 or more in appearance fees.

The Bottom Line Is Success

While there are substantial financial and career benefits to competing, the unspoken motivation that inspires many women to pursue the crown is the same competitive spirit that urges athletes to pursue Olympic medals or Super Bowl rings. Like all competitors, they prefer to reach for success and fall short, than to accept mediocrity.

Indeed, the quality that sets pageant contestants apart from the crowd is the desire to stretch themselves to their full potential. Laurel Schaefer, Miss America 1972, epitomizes the drive for achievement which motivates so many contestants. "I wanted to have an extraordinary destiny, something very special in life," she says. Her advice to young women who aspire to the crown is, "Establish your priorities and values. If you seek a life that is *extra* ordinary, you've got to live an exemplary life."

The bottom line is that the quest for the crown is not only about that tearful victory-walk down an illuminated runway with the crown and roses. Pageantry, ultimately, is about using the process of competition to pursue and achieve an extraordinary life personally and professionally.

Your First Steps on the Road to the Crown

The women who win have one thing in common.
They made the least mistakes,
and they were the best prepared.
DAVID BARTLEY, IMAGE SPECIALIST
AND PHOTOGRAPHER TO THE QUEENS

The road to the crown begins with a simple childhood fantasy, referred to as "the dream of a million girls" by the famous pageant coronation song, "There She Is." The appeal of that dream of gliding down the runway with the glittering crown and roses is that the tantalizing fantasy *can* become reality. Whether the title is Miss T.E.E.N, Miss USA, America's Junior Miss, Miss Universe, or Miss World, several lucky young women earn those coveted titles each year. As contestants appreciate, the quest for the crown is not merely a fantasy but an achievable dream. "When girls come in they tell me, 'I've dreamed about this since I was five years old!'" observes Kathleen Munson, a pageant consultant who has coached numerous state and national titleholders. "They want to live the fairy tale." Someone reading this book will.

But it takes more than a wave of a magic wand to live this modern-day fairy tale. Transforming the dream of winning a pageant title into reality requires knowledge of what it takes to win, consistent hard work to develop those qualities, practice to perfect presentation, and effective strategies for success. "The ones who are the most prepared, who have all the bases covered going in, are the ones who are the most successful," asserts David Bartley, a noted pageant photographer who has worked with numerous state and national-level titleholders. Any young woman from any part of the country who is willing to invest the time and effort to develop her potential fully can transform her dreams into reality. It's a matter of developing into a champion step-by-step.

Take the case of Kaye Lani Rae Rafko, Miss America 1988, a registered nurse and the daughter of a used auto parts dealer. "I was just the girl next door," she says, "just like everyone dreams about. . . . I wanted people to realize that it *can* happen to anyone—and I am an example that it does happen to anyone."

Jill St. Pierre, a high school classmate of Kaye Lani, had a unique vantage point to observe that transformation. As the reigning Miss Monroe County, Jill crowned a seventeen-year-old Kaye Lani as her successor. It was Rafko's first pageant and the victory that launched her six-year journey to the national runway. After watching Kaye Lani transform herself from a shy teenager into a national titleholder, Jill is convinced that "the girl who wins is just like you or I—just a girl next door. But with all the polish, the makeup, the hair, the gowns, the lights, and the adrenaline that night, that girl becomes Cinderella. It's intimidating to sit back as a little girl or teenager and watch that girl win, but it's important that girls realize that no matter how gorgeous, talented, and smart the girl who wins that night may appear, she is *just like them*. Yes, she has all these wonderful qualities—but so do they. They just need to be developed."

That process of development occurs when an entrant allows her childhood fantasy to evolve into an adult goal and backs it up with a sensible strategy to make that goal reality. It is simply a step-by-step, year-by-year growth process. The girls who eventually win aren't those who merely fantasize about walking the runway. They are the gutsy competitors who tirelessly work to *earn* the right to walk the runway. "With determination and hard work I was able to achieve goals and go much farther than I could have possibly imagined and I was crowned Miss America," says Rafko. "Nothing was handed to me on a silver platter. I worked hard at everything I have ever achieved."

That step-by-step growth process that leads to the throne begins at one of thousands of entry-level contests held each year. "At the local level you receive one coat of polish," explains Kylene Barker, Miss America 1979. "If you win and go on to the state level, you receive another coat of polish. Then if you win and go to the national level, you receive another coat of polish. But at each level, even if you don't happen to walk away with that crown, you really gain so much."

Whether you are a newcomer or an experienced contestant, achieving your goals comes down to this: Get started, develop yourself step-by-step, and enter again and again and again in pursuit of your dream. "Down South we put contestants on a 'four-year plan,'" observes Kathleen Munson. "Enter the first year to see if it's an experience you enjoy. Enter the second year with the idea of making the top ten. Enter the third year with the idea of making the top five. Enter the fourth year with the expectation of winning the pageant and going on to do well at the nationals. Don't plan to enter a pageant the first year and win the national title," she says. "You've got to know what you need to work toward."

As you start your quest for the crown, keep in mind that becoming a pageant winner is a process. First you dream. Then you work to make it happen.

1 · Find Your Unique Pathway to the Crown

But, where, when, and how does that step-by-step process begin, you may ask. At what age should I begin competing? Where do I start? How long will it take to win? The answer is, there is no "one-size-fits-all" blueprint for becoming a pageant winner. Each titleholder's road to the rhinestones is as unique as the woman who earns that crown.

At what age should I begin?

Let's consider the question of when to begin competing. It depends on the individual. Some contestants hit the runway as soon as they're out of diapers. Susan Akin, Miss America 1986, began entering pageants in elementary school, won the Little Miss America title, and later competed in over a hundred pageants. However, her experience is the exception to the rule. The backgrounds of major titleholders reveal that competing in children's and preteen pageants does *not* improve a young woman's chances of winning a major title like Miss America or Miss USA.

In fact, most national and international winners first competed during high school. A girl who enters her first pageant as a high school freshman has years ahead of her to participate in teen pageants, accumulate scholarships for college, and develop as a contestant. Many pageants have been developed especially for high school students, including America's Junior Miss (for high school seniors), Miss T.E.E.N., Miss Teen of America, and Miss Teen USA. Today, most contestants begin their quest for the crown between junior high school and their freshman year of college.

Even "late bloomers" can succeed. Students who enter their first contest as college sophomores still have four to six years to compete in adult pageants like Miss America and Miss USA, which have age cut-offs of twenty-four to twenty-six years. For example, Debra Maffett entered her first pageant as a twenty-one-year-old college student and lost for four years before winning the 1983 Miss America title as a twenty-five-year-old college graduate.

Women who missed the pageant experience entirely during their school years can enter events developed especially for older women. Mother-daughter contests and "Mrs." pageants are two of the most popular pageants for women who once assumed they were past their pageant prime. One recent winner, Sandra Earnest, a mother of ten children, began competing at age forty and won the 1993 Mrs. USA title as a forty-four-year-old! Pageants like Beauties of America feature multiple age categories for single, married, or divorced women ages twenty to sixty-plus. Others, like Most Glamorous Grandmother and Ms. Senior America, celebrate the beauty of senior citizens. Pageantry has a place for entrants of every age, advises Kathleen Munson, who quips, "We've got cradle-to-death pageants!" So, whatever your stage of life, it's never too late to embark on your quest for the crown.

How long will it take to win?

How long it takes to win the crown depends on the individual. Sandra Earnest won the Mrs. USA title on her third try, while Miss Americas Cheryl Prewitt (1980), Kaye Lani Rae Rafko (1988), and Debbye Turner (1990) each competed and lost for a half-a-decade before earning their coveted crowns. Fellow titleholders Tawny Godin (1976), Dorothy Benham (1977), Gretchen Carlson (1989), and Kimberly Aiken (1994) won the national title the first year they entered, as did Miss USAs Courtney Gibbs (1988) and Gretchen Polhemus (1989), and Miss Universe 1993, Dayanara Torres. You can win on your first try. You can win after years of losing. The time it takes to win is different for every contestant.

Where do I start?

The first step on your road to the crown is finding competitions to enter. It shouldn't be hard since an estimated 750,000 pageants are held annually in the United States alone.

The easiest pageants to enter are "theme" contests held locally to select school or college queens, football queens, festival and fair queens, convention queens, parade queens, and product queens ranging from Garlic Queen to Pork Princess. These are ideal for beginners to enter to gain experience.

Then there are the major pageant systems, like Miss America and America's Junior Miss, that start at the local level and lead to a national title. A contestant enters a local pageant held in her hometown or college. These locals can be "closed" (you must live in that town or attend that college), "semi-closed" (you must live within a certain radius, usually seventy-five miles), or "open" (any girl in the state can enter). The girl who wins the local title competes in the state contest, and that state winner goes on to the national competition. Such major pageant systems are helpful for anyone from beginners who need to gain experience to advanced contestants who hope to move up the runway to win a national title.

Other national or regional contests, usually those that are less established, invite "at-large" entries. Organizers select qualified contestants from mail-in applications and designate each as a representative of a city, county, state, or geographic region, which qualifies them to compete in the upper-level pageant. The Miss Teen of America and Miss Black America pageants allow at-large entries. Similarly, contestants for *'TEEN* magazine's Miss Teenage America Pageant are chosen from mail-in entries submitted by readers nationwide. Organizers select a dozen finalists and fly them to California to compete in the national finals, where Miss Teenage America is chosen.

Some state pageants also accept at-large entries rather than conducting local contests. For instance, girls who wish to enter the Miss Florida-USA Pageant submit an application, pay an entry fee if they are accepted as a contestant, and compete in a televised state contest. Whoever wins there represents her state in the Miss USA Pageant. Because at-large pageants are often easier to enter, they help a contestant to gain experience competing at the state or national level without having to battle up an ultra- competitive three-level system.

As you look for competitions to enter, keep in mind that pageants differ in their business status. Some are run by non-profit civic organizations to offer girls in their communities opportunities for personal growth and scholarships. They rarely charge entry fees, although entrants may be asked to sell program-book ads. Often, these nonprofit groups award scholarships to the winner and finalists. Other pageants are money-making ventures staged by businesses. Contestants are charged entry fees or sponsor fees ranging from $500 to $1,000 or more. Entrants can either pay the fee themselves, hold fundraisers, or find a sponsoring business to put up the money.

Neither a nonprofit or for-profit status guarantees that a pageant will be a quality event, so always check the organization's reputation before signing any agreement or paying an entry fee. Contact previous winners or contestants to ask if their experiences were positive, or contact a Better Business Bureau or Department of Consumer Protection to ask if complaints have been filed or legal action taken against the pageant.

With some effort and persistence, and a few necessary precautions, you should be able to find reputable, exciting pageants to enter.

Ultimately, when, where, and how you start your quest for the crown will depend on what works for you. Just as every winner's experience has been different, your own road to the crown will be as individual and unique as you are.

2 · Find the Right Pageant for Your Skills and Style

One of the most important secrets to success is finding the right "fit" between contestant and contest. Pageants differ radically in their philosophies, ranging from "beauty contests" that look for a beautiful, shapely winner with commercial appeal, to serious "scholarship/talent pageants" that seek accomplished winners to serve as role models for American youth. Their judging differs accordingly, ranging from scoring based on physical beauty alone, to scoring based on intelligence, talent, grades, community service, and physical fitness.

Beauty pageants usually view themselves as a launch-pad for the glamour careers (modeling, television, films), and thus emphasize beauty of face and figure, personality, and ability to communicate before an audience. Such pageants include Miss USA, Miss Universe, Miss Teen USA, Miss Teen All American, GuyRex's Miss United States, Miss World, and Mrs. America, among others. The judging is usually evenly divided between swimsuit, evening gown, and interview (private, then onstage), with a final question often determining the winner.

Scholarship pageants view themselves as personal development and leadership programs for female students and judge a wider range of qualities. For example, the Miss America scholarship pageant judges talent (40 percent), interview (30 percent), "physical fitness in swimsuit" (15 percent), evening wear (15 percent), and an on-stage interview during the finals (10 percent). A new emphasis on community service requires contestants to submit a written essay on a meaningful social issue she will address as the winner. Although not judged, per se, these platforms help judges determine which entrants demonstrate the leadership to serve as role models for women.

Another scholarship pageant, the America's Junior Miss Program for high school seniors, has five categories: interview (30 percent), scholastic achievement (20 percent), creative and performing arts (20 percent), fitness (15 percent) and presence and composure (15 percent). Similarly, the Miss T.E.E.N. and Teen of America Scholarship and Recognition pageants judge scholastic achievement, volunteer service, creative arts (speech/skill/hobby/talent), personal interview, and formal presentation, usually of equal weight. *'TEEN* magazine's Miss Teenage America Pageant judges entrants on leadership, community service, scholastic achievement, poise, and appearance. These teen scholarship pageants do not include swimsuit competitions.

To win, match your strengths to the pageant's judging emphasis. Determine what type of winner that pageant is looking for: a gorgeous spokesperson; a perky, fashionable teen-queen; or an accomplished role model for women. "Like any other undertaking in life, you've got to find your niche," advises Mike Fifrick, a 1991 Miss World judge. "Everyone has talent and skills in life. You've got to find those and become successful in the area of *your* talents and gifts."

Consider New Mexico's Mai Shanley. Mai failed to make the top ten at the 1982 Miss America Pageant, then entered the Miss USA Pageant—and won. The Miss USA image and judging criteria matched Mai's strengths. Finding the right "fit" for her qualities paid off. Likewise, Shawn Weatherly's drop-dead good looks were a mismatch for Miss America, where she lost at the state level. Yet Shawn won the 1980 Miss USA and Miss Universe crowns by a landslide. She found her fit. Girls whose strongest assets are their gorgeous face and figure fare better in bona fide beauty contests like Miss USA, Miss Teen USA, and Miss Universe, which emphasize beauty and personality.

High school students with talent, good grades, and a resume of community service fare well in scholarship pageants like

America's Junior Miss, Miss Teenage America, Miss T.E.E.N., and Miss Teen of America which judge school grades, honors, volunteerism, skills and talents, and speaking—but *not* swimsuit. Girls who succeed in scholarship pageants would probably be a mismatch for Miss Teen USA, which bases two-thirds of scoring on physical beauty.

College women with strong speaking skills and stage talents do well in the Miss America system, which emphasizes talent and interview (70 percent). Miss America 1989, Gretchen Carlson, though attractive, was not a typical "beauty queen." A valedictorian, Stanford honor student, and award-winning violinist, her strongest assets—brains and talent—were a perfect "fit" for "scholarship" judging. Swimsuit, her weakest point, was only 15 percent of scoring. Although she won Miss America, Gretchen wouldn't have fared as well at Miss USA, where the judging criteria and image would have worked against her.

As these winners demonstrate, the secret to increasing your odds of success is knowing your strengths and entering pageants that look for those qualities. Find your "fit."

3 · Use Your Entry Form to Create a Winning Image

"Look your best on paper!" says Kathleen Munson, a pageant consultant. Your entry form is an application for a job that could change your life. Entry forms, also called applications, résumés, or fact sheets, are "sales brochures" of personal, academic, and professional information used in judges' notebooks to help them get to know the contestants.

As the judges' first impression of your qualifications for the "job," your entry form should be impeccable. Make copies of the entry form and practice filling it out. List hobbies, awards, and honors as they come to mind. Keep revising until you come up with a draft copy that presents you at your best. Proofread it for spelling and accuracy. (Some judges ask about entry-form errors: "Tell me, Miss So- and-So, what is 'zong-dis-tance running?'") Type the final version on the original entry form. Make sure the finished product is neat, pleasing to the eye, and goof-proof.

A fact sheet is your "verbal snapshot," revealing to judges who you are. It should present you as a well-rounded individual with *diverse* interests and impressive accomplishments.

Fact Sheets "Lead" the Judges and Emcee

Since judges use the fact sheets to come up with questions for the personal interviews, a contestant's information should be as interesting as possible to "invent" possibilities for questions and guide the judges to subjects she feels comfortable discussing. "One of the keys to preparing for an interview is your résumé," advises Kim Boyce, Miss Florida 1983, adding "The judges will usually find their questions from the résumé, so don't put anything on there that you don't want them to ask you about. I could tell that the judges took the time before they ever got to the pageant to look for questions that pertained. Have an interesting résumé that is purely truthful so the judges have something to ask you about."

Susan Akin, Miss America 1986, mentioned her mean pet monkey, pet lions "Radar" and "Herman" (who was killed by poisoned meat), and her favorite hobby—magic. The national panel not only *asked* her about her odd pet menagerie, they asked her to *demonstrate* some magic (which is against the rules, but who's going to argue with judges!). Anticipating that a request might arise, she came prepared, pulled trick strings from her pocket, performed some "magic," and cast her spell on the judges. She won.

Since fact sheets are also used to derive questions for onstage interviews with the host, interesting or impressive information can distinguish a girl from her competitors. When Bob Barker chatted with Minnesota's Barbara Peterson in 1976, he brought up her father being a state associate supreme court judge, her fluency in Swedish, triple major, and plans to enter law school. Barbara was as impressive on paper as she was in person, and judges awarded her the Miss USA crown.

At the 1993 Miss Teen USA Pageant, the emcee, Dick Clark, asked Vermont's Charlotte Lopez to discuss her thirteen years as a foster child, her upcoming book *Lost in the System*, and her impending adoption as a near-adult. Those facts gave her a distinct and unforgettable image and helped her earn the Miss Teen USA title.

In the Miss America system, because each titleholder represents a scholarship program and supports a cause during her reign, her fact sheet should emphasize her academic accomplishments and community service. If selected for the top five, she will be brought onstage to discuss her "platform." Past titleholders Leanza Cornett and Kimberly Aiken each won the crown after their superb onstage discussions about their platforms, AIDS education and homeless.

Private interviews and onstage interviews are brief, so don't put anything on your entry form that you don't want to waste time talking about during judging. List information that invites the judges and emcee to ask you questions that present you as an interesting, accomplished young woman.

Making Your Résumé Better

Since so many fact-sheet entries can sound bland on paper, phrase them creatively. If your hobby is "reading," personalize it: "reading Civil War history books," "reading autobiographies of great Americans," etcetera. If you're athletic, don't merely list "sports." Give that activity *impact*: "1,000-meter champion in track and field," "long-distance running in charity fundraiser marathons." The hobby, interest, or sport should pique judges' interest.

Use your résumé to focus judges' attention on the experiences, accomplishments, and skills that make you a fascinating person. Winners' entries have included:

- Miss USA 1989—cattle and horse broker
- Miss Universe 1976—Israeli military glider pilot
- Miss America 1976—spoke six languages
- Miss America 1978—speech-writer for the Ohio State Senate
- Miss America 1993—played "Ariel" at Disney MGM Studios

Stretching the Truth Can Backfire

Don't stretch the truth. An entry form that contains exaggerated claims can backfire. "When you read résumés, you read a lot of wonderful things," remarks Vernon DeSear, a past Miss Florida officer and state and national judge. "Sometimes I will question them to see if it's all [truthful] or not. For example, some girls put that they want to be an attorney. So you ask them about the classes they're taking or what motivates them to achieve that—and *nothing fits*! They just thought 'attorney' looked good on the résumé." He adds laughing, "They're gonna be found out *real quick* when they don't know anything about law. I think their [lack of] credibility comes out eventually."

Since stretching the truth is common, some pageants instruct judges not to place much credence on the entry forms. "I tell my judges, 'You know, a parent may have filled that out!'" says Paula Miles, who operates six Miss USA/Teen USA state pageants. "It may not always be 'accurate,'" she says, chuckling. Great fact sheet or not, the winning ingredient is the *woman*. "The girls like to feel like we're delving in and finding out about them, but it's not what they write on the paper that wins. The girls sell themselves."

Still, don't underestimate the impact a quality résumé can have upon the judges.

4 · Create Winning "Paper Work"

In addition to a portrait, many scholarship pageants require entrants to submit "paper work," which can count for as much as 60 percent of scoring in some programs. Paper work can include essays on worthy causes, school transcripts, résumés of scholastic achievements, community service records, or a test of general knowledge.

School Transcripts and Knowledge Tests

Some scholarship pageants for teenagers, Like America's Junior Miss, Miss Teen of America, Miss Teenage America, and Miss T.E.E.N., require school transcripts for judging on academic achievement. "They must have a B-or-above grade point average," says Lori Moore, of *'TEEN* magazine, sponsors of Miss Teenage America. "Those who make the top forty are required to send their school transcript."

How are scholastic categories evaluated? "There are two panels of judges," explains Robert Hedberg, of the America's Junior Miss program. "A separate panel of five judges evaluates the scholastic-achievement category which is based strictly on their high school transcripts. The judges are individuals qualified and trained in evaluating transcripts, such as guidance counselors and college admissions people."

What do they judge? According to Warren Alexander, national director of Miss Teen of America, "Judges consider class rank, grade point average, the nature of the classes taken, and any special activities related to the scholarly process. Does she suggest, 'I *love* learning and knowledge'?"

What if contestants don't have terrific grades? "I'd hate to ward off kids because maybe their grades aren't the highest," admits Hedberg. "When I talk to kids who say, 'Well, my grades aren't that good,' what I try to instill in them is that there are *five* categories. Many people who advanced in the program did not receive any points in one category but were stronger in others. I encourage them that even if they have lower grades, we are a scholarship program—not a 'scholastics' program." Don't panic over submitting your grades.

The Miss Teen of America program also has a "general awareness" category that involves a written test of entrants' awareness of teen interests, contemporary issues, politics, sports, television, films, and the like.

Essays and Issues Platforms

The Miss America Organization had developed a community service program to "encourage young women to explore the relevant social issues of their times . . . that inspire their interest and devotion." Every entrant is required to submit a written essay on an issue she has a special interest in. The titleholder then champions that cause as her official "platform" during her year of service. Carolyn Sapp (1992) worked closely with the U.S. Department of Education, Leanza Cornett (1993) lobbied Congress and helped raise over one million dollars for AIDS, and Kimberly Aiken (1994) worked with H.U.D. and Habitat for Humanity. As Marjorie Vincent, Miss America 1991, explained, "The most rewarding part of this year has been being able to use the crown and the visibility associated with the crown to help a lot of people in need." Worthy causes championed by recent titleholders have included:

- nursing and hospice care
- motivating youth to excellence
- ending domestic violence

- education
- AIDS education and prevention
- homelessness
- youth motivation

Although the essays are *not* scored, judges do ask each contestant in-depth questions about her platform. A young woman's knowledge of her cause and commitment to benefiting her community can have a great impact on the judges—and who ultimately wins. When selecting a platform, select a cause that is meaningful to *you*. Make sure you can back up everything you include in your essay and discuss why that cause is important to you and what you are doing to further it.

Community Service Résumés

Many pageants require entrants to submit résumés of their community volunteer service. In the Miss Teen of America and Miss T.E.E.N. programs, judges actually score contestants' contributions to school and community. Judges in the America's Junior Miss and Miss Teenage America pageants consider commitment to volunteerism during interview judging. *'TEEN* spokesperson Lori Moore explains, "We ask the teens to submit to us a list of ways they have helped their community, such as participating in community service programs, outreach programs through their school or church, or in environmental cleanup and recycling programs."

Competing in this category requires *involvement*. "You'd better start to do some things in your community and school," advises Kathleen Munson. "Run for student body president, try out for the soccer team, visit hospitals. You need to find what you can do to help your community. Become a more dimensional person. Don't be a 'one-act play'!"

Platform essays, school transcripts, awareness tests, community service resumes, and fact sheets help judges to recognize and reward the academic achievements and contributions to society that distinguish girls as leaders. Use your "paper work" to present yourself as a winner.

5 · Sell Yourself With a Winning Photograph

Pageants require entrants to submit photographs for the judges' notebooks and program book. Like her entry form, a contestant's photo is her introduction to judges. As such, it is a valuable tool she can use to convince them she's the one to wear the crown. "Your photo is competing in your place. It may be the first impression the judges have of you," explains Terry Atwood, a pageant photography specialist who has photographed numerous state winners, including several national runners-up.

Pageant photos are almost always "head shots," head-and-shoulders poses with direct eye contact. Beauty contests like Miss USA/Teen USA ask for a glamorous black-and-white head shot without a crown. Teen scholarship pageants request a head shot reflecting an all American look, and the Miss America system prefers head shots with more of a career look. Photos for teens should suit the age. "A teenager should look like a teenager," says Terry Atwood. "They should still have that ingenue look, rather than a professional model look. Try to make them look the right age—not ten years older."

Pageant photos for any age group should always be top quality. Contestants don't get a second chance to make a great first impression with judges. "A great photograph is another plus for them." explains David Bartley, of Images Photography by David Bartley. It can't be so *over*flattering that judges are disappointed when they meet the girl, or so unattractive that they have an unfavorable impression when they look at her photo. "It has to be the *best version* of you." An unflattering photo of a recent top contender for a major title damaged her chances—but the *winner's* photo was picture perfect. "The photo isn't what made her win," says David, "but it set her in a good light so when she hit the process, her first step was well taken care of."

"It needs to be a best-case reflection of them," he emphasizes. "When I'm doing 'graduate-level' work, the Miss America, Miss USA stuff, these women need to look fairly assertive. They need to look like they really have something going on behind those eyes. The attitude that you take into the shoot is the attitude the film is going to see. You need to have feelings inside that will generate the kind of look you are looking for."

The image in the final photo depends upon the accessories used for the photo shoot. Atwood and Bartley experiment with different necklines, hairstyles, and earrings to *create* a winning image for clients. (See photo tips on next page.)

Correct cosmetics are also critical. To avoid a clownish look, David recommends that contestants avoid bright makeup for their photo sittings. "I am not in favor of strong colors on a face—period. I was using neutral shades before it became popular." He has found that the soft, neutral shades that blend well with skin tones give a clean, flattering look on film—and in person.

Further, Bartley urges his clients to use their pageant photos as a tool first to *create*, then maintain, a winning image. "If they've got the look that they want in their photograph, stick an eight-by-ten on the mirror and work at that look."

There is no question that expert photography can offer a winning edge, but specialists can be too expensive for a local entrant. Until they compete on a more advanced level, girls on a budget can bring a state or national program book to a reputable local photographer and ask if he can reproduce the same style of head shot. "See examples of what they've done," David advises. "You need to be comfortable with this person because you are going to totally stick your ego on the line."

Tips for Winning Photos:

- Make sure your photos look like you will at the pageant.
- If you change your hair color or style, or "improve" your nose or teeth, get an updated photo.
- Use frontal "glamour" lighting to "wash out" shadows.
- Hair color should stand out against the backdrop.
- Earrings help draw attention onto the face and eyes. Medium-to-large rhinestone, crystal, pearl, or gold earrings work best. Choose classic or elegant styles.
- To create a glamour look for a beauty pageant photo, try a beaded neckline and crystal cocktail earrings.
- For a "California girl" image for beauty pageants, try fan-blown hair and casual attire. Western wear or a button-down shirt over a T-shirt work well.
- For a career look suitable for scholarship pageants, wear a classic suit jacket and conservative blouse.
- To create a regal look for any pageant, try bare shoulders, hair worn up, and elegant crystal earrings.
- Never use a scenic (forest, library, etc.) backdrop.
- Try not to use color photos for black and white program books. They can reproduce less attractively.

According to Terry Atwood, the perfect pageant head shot is, "classic and timeless, with a clean, smooth background, where the person is recognizable, and looks elegant and confident, and her best features are accented. If I see that in a photograph, then I feel I have a winning photograph."

First impressions last, so start your road to the crown successfully by convincing the judges that you are a winner *before* they meet you. Make sure that every item you submit prior to the competition—from a flawless entry form to a flattering photograph—creates the image of a winner.

The Winning "Package"

You're judging the total girl.
Does she have the total package?
RICHARD GUY, GUYREX ASSOCIATES

What do judges look for in a winner? Naturally, the exact qualities judges seek will differ from judge to judge, pageant to pageant, and year to year, but there is one overall quality *every* judge seeks: a "winning package." Brian Boitano, an Olympic gold medalist and national judge, expressed it this way, "You have to go for a *package*, someone who is going to be strong and will be able to take the heat."

Ultimately, a winner stands out from the crowd of competitors because she exemplifies success in every area of her life. It's not enough to demonstrate expertise in interview, evening gown, swimsuit, and talent. A serious candidate for the crown must also possess two important, but less tangible, qualities: a winning *attitude* and a winning *image*.

THE WINNING ATTITUDE

Attitude is everything in competition. A positive attitude can help a girl surmount disadvantages and personal obstacles to take that glorious victory walk down the runway. It will enable her to believe in herself when others can't see her potential, to choose behavior that will further her goals, and to turn discouraging "failures" into eventual victory. A winning attitude is the quality that transforms a competitor into a champion.

6 · Never Underestimate Your Potential

Having a winning attitude means never underestimating your potential. A girl's disadvantaged upbringing, poverty, serious illness, physical "handicaps," or past tragedies are no indication of her potential for the future. Dozens of young women have overcome enormous personal obstacles to achieve great success in pageants.

- After surviving a near-fatal car accident, mangled leg, and over one hundred stitches in her face, Cheryl Prewitt won the 1980 Miss America title.
- Miss Universe 1970, Marisol Malaret, was orphaned at age ten and raised by an impoverished, elderly aunt.
- After undergoing a double mastectomy, Joan Sewall won the 1981 Mrs. Minnesota title and made the top ten at Mrs. America.
- Mary Gainey overcame multiple birth defects and five operations to become Miss South Carolina and first runner-up to Miss America 1991.
- Carol Gist, who was born out of wedlock and raised by her mother in Detroit's inner-city, became Miss USA 1990 and 1st runner-up to Miss Universe.
- Michelle Kline made the top ten at Miss America a year after undergoing a kidney transplant.
- Jennifer Wall mastered classical piano and made the top ten at Miss America—despite being hearing-impaired.
- Miss Teen USA 1993, Charlotte Lopez, was a foster child who had lived with six families over thirteen years.

- After surviving cancer, Terri Sue Liford became Miss Michigan and competed at Miss America with a wig to conceal her hair loss from chemotherapy.
- Kimberly Aiken survived a life-threatening aneuryism and brain surgery at age eleven to become Miss America 1994.
- Miss 1992 World-America, Sharon Beldon, was an orphan.

As these winners prove, even the most devastating circumstances needn't limit a girl's ability to be a champion. The inspirational proof is Heather Whitestone, who won the 1995 Miss America title despite being deaf since infancy. The remarkable young woman read the judges' lips during her personal interview and performed a classical ballet to music she couldn't hear by memorizing the beats. Heather attributes her winning attitude to her mother's advice: "Remember, the last four letters in American are 'I CAN'!" Only hard work and perseverance can determine how much she can ultimately accomplish. Whatever personal obstacles you face as you pursue the crown, never underestimate your potential.

7 · Know Yourself, Be Yourself, Be Your Best

To be a winner on the runway and off, you've got to know yourself, be yourself, and be your best. Unfortunately, many entrants underrate the importance of such individuality. "Be real," advises Sam Haskell, a respected national judge. "Be different. Be who you are, and not who you think they want you to be. Try to show the judges the *real* you," he emphasizes.

To stand out in a crowd of outstanding contestants a girl must radiate the qualities of a champion. A champion never blends in with the crowd. She *stands out* in judges' minds because she projects an unforgettable personal style. "Winners are themselves," says image specialist David Bartley. "They're not clones. They don't attempt to be somebody else. They attempt to be the best version of themselves."

But for a contestant to successfully radiate winning individuality, she must first "discover" herself. "Be in touch with who you are, what you are, and why you are," advises Jeff Bell, a veteran pageant director and magazine executive. "Where have you come from? Who are the people you most admire? How have they affected your life? What have you accomplished? What do you *want* to accomplish? What is ahead for you in life?" The downfall of many women," he contends, "is that they don't know themselves. You need to pray or meditate to get in touch with who you are. Get to know yourself. I know it sounds hokey. You hear so many out-going queens say, 'Be yourself.' But it's so true; *know* yourself and *be* yourself."

Kaye Lani Rae Rafko's success confirms the value of just being who you *are*. A Tahitian-dancing oncology nurse from Michigan, with a whimsical Hawaiian name, she seemed about as likely to win the crown as a snowball rolling down Hell's runway. "I was a longshot. People did not expect me to win. People had encouraged me to change, but my attitude was, 'I'm not going to change for anyone. I'm just going to be Kaye Lani and if they don't like who Kaye Lani is—tough petunias!'" she says, chuckling. As it turned out, Rafko's uniqueness delighted the judges. She not only was selected Miss America 1988—she became one of the all-time greats. "The only advice I would give a contestant," she says confidently, "is just be *herself*."

Likewise, Kristin Huffman, Miss Ohio 1989 and fourth runner-up to Miss America, also succeeded by emphasizing her distinct style. "I have a quote that I use from the late Sir Laurence Olivier: 'Don't be afraid to be outrageous or daring or different. They'll shoot you down anyway—so let it all out.' I *am* different," she affirms, "and I'm not afraid of that. You'll always notice somebody who's different. But it shouldn't be: 'I want

Miss Universe 1994
Sushmita Sen.

Miss Teen USA 1994
Shauna Gambill.

Miss USA 1994
Lu Parker.

Miss Teenage America 1994
Elizabeth Andre.

American's Junior Miss for 1993
Rebecca Jones.

Miss 1992 World-America
Sharon Beldon.

Miss Teen All American 1994
SreeRatna Kancherla.

Mrs. International 1995
Margo Watson.

to be different so they'll notice me.' It should be: 'If I *am* different, make the most of it.'"

Many contestants turned their uniqueness into an asset. Jennifer Wall, Miss Washington 1989, was a hearing-impaired classical pianist who dared to be herself. An inspiring "original," she made the top ten at Miss America. Terri Utley, Miss Arkansas-USA 1982, broke the "can't win" rule for short hair and became the first short-haired Miss USA. Despite being both short, 5'3", and a classical violinist—*two* supposed "can't wins"—Gretchen Carlson remained herself and became Miss America 1989. Sher Patrick, Miss Ohio 1977, broke tradition by performing an exotic middle-eastern belly dance, delighted the judges with her uniqueness, and was named a runner-up to Miss America. Each of these women dared to be herself, had the courage to be an original, gracefully broke "can't win" traditions, and charmed their judges.

Contestants who blatantly copy previous winners miss the essence of the crown: the outstanding *individual*. "I look for what is real," says Sam Haskell. "You tend to overlook less than perfect if you see something there that is real." In fact, throughout pageant history, the most memorable winners have been those, like Diane Sawyer, Mary Ann Mobley, and Kaye Lani Rafko, who dared to be originals. Never try to earn the crown by squeezing into another woman's mold. Understand what makes *you* special and make the most of those qualities.

Knowing yourself, being yourself, and being your best are the keys to competing capably without regrets. "You should just be the way you are," Cecilia Bolocco, Miss Universe 1987, once stated. "That's the way I acted at the Miss Universe Pageant. I said, 'I'm just going to give my best and work as hard as I can, so then I won't have regrets if I don't make it because, if I don't win, that doesn't mean I'm a failure. That means the crown is not for me—and that's no big deal.'"

8 · Believe in Yourself When Others Don't

Be forewarned. As you are working to transform your dreams into reality, you will encounter skeptics who will not believe in you until after you've won. Meet the "I'll believe it when I see it" crowd.

Ask Kellye Cash and Kimberly Aiken, who lost local pageants just months before being crowned Miss Americas 1987 and 1994. Amazingly, their judges concluded that these young ladies, who each went on to become that year's Miss America, were not qualified to be local titleholders! Although both were disappointed at losing, they refused to allow that panel's opinion of them to shake their confidence. Instead, both immediately entered another local pageant, won, and shot to the national throne. By choosing to believe in themselves when others didn't, Kim and Kellye experienced the opportunity of a lifetime. After Kellye's victory, when reporters asked her advice for future entrants, she responded, "Dream big because you can *reach* your dreams!"

Kaye Lani Rae Rafko also encountered people whose poor opinions of her potential might have discouraged her from seeking the crown and cost her the experience of a lifetime. After she lost a state pageant, a respected judge told Kaye Lani that her Tahitian dancing was not a "real" talent and that if she hoped to win, she'd have to switch to singing. Fortunately, Kaye Lani chose to believe in herself when others didn't and became the first Tahitian dancer to win the Miss America title. So much for "expert" opinions!

As a young woman striving to achieve your dreams through pageants, you must refuse to allow your self-confidence to be undermined by other people's low opinions of your potential. If, like Kaye Lani and Kellye, you encounter people who doubt your potential and try to discourage you—ignore them. As

Vanessa Williams, who was asked to give up her crown, yet became a Grammy award winning vocalist, once put it, "You have to believe in yourself. If you don't, that's your downfall." Decide to believe in yourself when others don't. It could change your life.

9 · Choose Winning Behavior Day-by-Day

The most significant ingredient in achieving success is choosing winning behavior day-by-day. Make no mistake about it. The greatest difference between winners and losers in pageants—and life—is not merely natural talent. It is the seemingly insignificant choices made moment by moment each day. Those small choices become our habits, and our habits become our destiny. "It *isn't* natural ability," asserts Marilyn Van Derbur, an expert on motivation. "Natural ability can play a role—and does play a role all our lives—but when we excel, we excel because we have truly prepared ourselves over and over and over."

A case in point is Laurel Schaefer, whose life was dramatically transformed by her commitment to daily winning choices. "I always tenaciously pursued my dreams," she says. "I didn't have time to be flighty or frivolous. I had too many things to do. I was very aggressive about my future and I was very disciplined. Many times I would have to say no to social events . . . because I had more important things to do, whether it was dance class or private vocal lessons. I felt the destiny for my life. I knew what I had to do and I had no time to waste. . . . And deep down inside I always knew that someday, something very special was going to happen for me."

Similarly, Donna Axum, a former Miss America, also used daily winning choices to turn her dreams into reality. "I *knew* that I had it in me to win the Miss Arkansas title," she says. So to achieve her goals, she chose to pass up many of the pleasant diversions of campus life. "I was very focused," Donna recalls. "By that I mean that I didn't spend a lot of time in college learning to play bridge or using my time nonproductively. I was always working toward reaching my goals. I was at the music department vocalizing in the practice rooms or I was performing and traveling with the U-Arkettes. I was doing everything I could to sharpen my competitive skills." To reinforce her efforts she taped a motto on her mirror: "Decide what you want and then decide what you're willing to give up to achieve it."

These winners understood that effective daily choices actually determined the course of a life. Choose winning behavior day-by-day to make your dreams reality.

10 · Be Willing to Sweat for Success

When hard work is added to winning daily choices, even seemingly impossible dreams can be achieved! Cheryl Prewitt's commitment to hard work elevated her from the Miss Choctaw County stage to the 1980 Miss America runway. Yet initially she was totally unprepared for competition. "I entered fully expecting to win, but I didn't do a thing toward *working* for it," she recalls, "I didn't know how to walk, how to talk, and I wobbled in my high heels. I just didn't know anything about it—and I didn't win. I could have been discouraged, but then I began to realize that when you feel a dream down in your heart you don't sit back and wait for it to fall on you!" She chuckles. "You have to *work* for it! You have to begin to set that dream into motion and to do everything you can do to be the best at what you're trying to accomplish."

Hard work and discipline beyond what others are willing to do is the key to winning. During a conversation shortly after Debbye Turner won the 1990 Miss America title, her mother, Gussie Turner, described the back-breaking effort Debbye invested in capturing the crown. "When she trains for a pageant, she trains like a fighter," she exclaimed, "more determined, working harder. She trained for the Miss America Pageant harder than she trained for the Miss Missouri. She trained for Miss Missouri harder than for Miss Columbia. She worked hard and believed that her opportunity would come—and she wanted to be ready when it came. She prepared for seven years—and she *was* ready. Hard work pays."

As the experiences of these winners prove: Reaching the throne means investing the sweat-producing, muscle-fatiguing, emotion-draining hard work others aren't willing to push themselves to do. "It's not easy," admits Sharon Turrentine, a physical fitness specialist who has trained numerous titleholders. "Hey, if it was *easy* everybody would do it. It's that willingness to go that extra mile, to pay the price, to make yourself the best that you can be in all areas of competition. You've got to be prepared physically, mentally, and emotionally. With anything in life, you must always strive to go one step farther, one step farther—or you backslide. This is America and there is one thing that can stop you from achieving your dreams—and that is yourself. If you have a realistic goal and go for it one hundred percent, you are going to reach the heights you were destined for."

"It's almost like preparing for the Olympics," says Donna Axum, who now judges national pageants such as Miss America and America's Junior Miss. "It's mental, physical, and emotional training." Paying the price for success is what separates the girls on the runway from those in the audience.

11 · Visualize Your Way to Success

Closely observe participants in the Olympics and other major sports championships and you'll discover that winners supplement their physical training program with mental visualization. Pageant winners are no exception.

When Gretchen Carlson set her sights on a national crown, she not only set about training for each event, she prepared her mind to win. "I am a firm believer in visualizing how far you want to go in competition," she says. "If you visualize that you want to become part of the top ten, then you should see yourself lined up in the top ten. If you visualize yourself becoming [the winner] then you should see yourself walking down the runway. I believe that in the long run in any form of competition, maybe half of it is in the mind."

Research has proven that performance *is* improved when competitors supplement their training with visualization, but their mental exercises must focus on *each specific action*. A champion gymnast doesn't merely see herself standing on the medalists' platform; she mentally rehearses every step in her balance-beam routine. Likewise, a pageant competitor can't simply imagine herself being crowned. She should focus on performing flawlessly in each category of competition. The mental images must be realistic down to the smallest detail. For instance, to visualize your talent, actually feel yourself walk onstage, see the audience and the stage lights in your eyes, hear your music track, feel yourself confidently play to the judges as you perform your talent, hear the applause of the audience as the judges mark their ballots, and feel yourself nod to the judges and turn to leave the stage proudly. Perform that exercise regularly to prepare your mind to feel fully prepared and confident when that exciting moment in the spotlight finally arrives.

While such visualization exercises have helped to improve performance, relying on mental imaging instead of regular serious training will sabotage a contestant's chances. "A lot of times you see girls who are putting an awful lot into winning, but are not doing a whole lot of preparation," observes former Miss Arkansas, Christi Taunton. "They're doing a lot of it in their *minds*. Sure you have to see it in your mind and believe it before you can do it, but you have to do the homework too."

Preparing the mind to succeed is a proven benefit to a good training program, but without plenty of hard work to back it, those mental images will remain nothing more than tantalizing fantasies.

12 · Learn to Handle the Press

Like any entertainer, politician, or pro athlete, a titleholder has to be able to handle the press effectively. Whether it is during talk shows, press conferences, or media interviews, an ability to control the message you communicate to reporters is critical. "I respected the press," says Kaye Lani Rae Rafko, "because they were my best means of communication with the public, with America. I respected them, and in exchange, I think they were able to respect me. Overall, the press was wonderful to me."

Fortunately, most reporters are professional, ethical, and fair. However, other reporters approach pageants with negative preconceptions, hopes for a "hot" story, and no compunction about lifting remarks out of context to fit the slant of their story. A young woman who carelessly offers reporters colorful opinions can quickly find herself embroiled in controversy. In fact, several national contestants who innocently shared controversial views about premarital cohabitation and intimacy, and abortion during Pageant Week found themselves the focus of a media feeding frenzy that turned their experience into a nightmare.

Topics that require careful handling include:

- your virginity or sexual experiences
- abortion
- living together prior to marriage, premarital sex
- homosexuality
- past use of drugs or alcohol
- whether you have had cosmetic surgery

"Avoid controversial subjects as much as possible," advises Roger Knight, a judge, business executive, and retired Miss Florida officer. "You don't need to be totally paranoid, but you've got to exercise discretion. If they ask you something you don't want to answer—don't answer it. Don't have an opinion." Some titleholders use an automatic "no opinion" strategy to avoid controversy. Dorothy Benham, one of the most successful titleholders of all, was a master of the technique. When reporters goaded her, "Don't you have an opinion on *anything?*" she'd reply, "I've learned that the best thing is to keep them to myself."

Even Kaye Lani Rae Rafko, who reporters labeled "refreshingly outspoken," politely sidestepped issues she didn't wish to address. "Just because I have the Miss America crown on my head doesn't mean I have all the right answers," she'd say. "Even the president of the United States doesn't have all the right answers. I'm human. I don't have all the answers to every world situation or crisis." Her philosophy was simple: Be able to live with every word that leaves your mouth. "I answered what I wanted to," she admits. "I knew that everything I said to them could follow me—not only for the year, but for the rest of my life."

Be especially careful about speaking "off the record." Several years ago, a Miss Florida shared insiders' gossip about the national winner, assuming that her remarks were off the record. Instead, she was quoted in papers from coast to coast with a predictable "sour grapes" slant. She eventually apologized on *Larry King Live*. Anything that you say within earshot of a reporter is considered fair game for publication. If you wouldn't want to see it in headlines, don't say it.

That's *not* to say that today's contestants should not hold opinions about the issues of the day. Any young woman who aspires to represent her community, state, or country should have a broad knowledge of social issues, politics, and current events to be able to express her views capably on those subjects in public. But phrase remarks made to reporters thoughtfully, intelligently, and diplomatically to avoid controversy that might cause judges to think twice about awarding you an important title.

If you are selected as the winner, your year in the spotlight will require unfailing self-confidence, stamina, and verbal poise. A winning attitude enables you to be at your best mentally while preparing, competing, and reigning.

THE WINNING IMAGE

Unlike a winning attitude, which involves inner qualities, a winning image involves *external* qualities—a contestant's image and appearance. Because a titleholder is a spokesperson for the pageant and a role model for girls, how she presents herself is important. Therefore, from the moment judges meet an entrant they carefully scrutinize her appearance from head to toe to determine if she possesses a winning image to compliment the crown.

13 · Know the Image of the Pageant You Enter

Pageants are not all the same. Each pageant has its own distinct "look." To win, a contestant has to achieve a balance, both being herself and conveying the image of the title she hopes to win. "Know the system. There is definitely an 'image' for each pageant," explains Kathleen Munson, a pageant consultant and former head of the Midwest Judges Certification Program. "There is a difference between the Miss America system and

Costuming should match the pageant's *image*.
Here, Texas' Christy Fichter won the 1986 Miss USA
crown with suitably sexy westernwear
(GUYREX ASSOCIATES, INC.).

Florida's Joanna Bramos, 1991 Miss Teen of America, represented "great state achiever" Lewis Carroll, author of *Alice in Wonderland*.

the Miss USA system, and with the teen pageants and Mrs. pageants. For instance, there is a much greater emphasis on glamour and drama in the Miss USA look, and Miss Teen USA follows Miss USA. Mrs. America is a 'Miss USA look,' and

Mrs. USI (United States International) is a 'Miss America look.' They each have a definite 'look.'"

Understanding the pageant's image will help a contestant craft her most suitable look for competition. "The first thing you have to do is know what you are looking for," advises David Bartley, an image specialist. "When I am [preparing] a girl for Miss America, I am basically going for a television anchor-woman look: stylish, fresh, classic—a woman who looks like she is going places. When I am working with a girl for Miss USA, they are more fashion-forward, more glamorous in the traditional sense. It's more of a model's look. Different pageants have different looks."

Once the contestant understands the general image of the pageant she is entering, she should tailor her hairstyle and wardrobing to 1) look her best and 2) convey the image of that pageant. Miss USA is sexy, busty, and glamorous, so a young woman who hopes to win that title should create her sexiest, most glamorous look. Scholarship pageants want a classic, wholesome titleholder so a contestant should go with her most wholesome, classically elegant look. In each case, the young woman remains herself, but presents herself with the 'look' appropriate for *that* pageant.

It's a little like an actress auditioning for different film roles. A contestant is auditioning for a *specific role*. Understand the overall image of the pageant you're entering and create your own winning look *within* that general image:

Miss America: Classic beauty, intelligent, stage talent, great public speaker, civic volunteer, elegant evening-gown look, usually mid-length or upswept hair, wholesome figure (5'3" to 5'11").

Miss USA: Gorgeous face, vivacious personality, good conversationalist, glamorous evening-gown look, long or upswept hair, sexy, busty, leggy figure (5'6" to 6'0").

Miss Universe: Multiethnic look, classically beautiful face, often regal, poised speaker, hair down over shoulders or upswept, pretty but nonvoluptuous figure (5'2" to 5'11").

Miss Teen USA: Youthfully pretty look; great smile; friendly personality, sense of humor; glamorous, but simpler evening-gown look; well-toned figure (5'3" to 5'10").

America's Junior Miss / Miss Teen Of America: Wholesome girl-next-door image; intelligent; pretty; good student; well-spoken; good role model; community volunteer; holds lofty career goals; simple; pretty evening gown look.

Miss T.E.E.N.: Very similar to the above wholesome teen titles, but *slightly* more glamorous; a "teenage Miss America" look.

Leanza Cornett, Miss America 1993, is an example of a title-holder who understands how to adjust her image to fit the situation. When I judged Leanza at the national pageant, she presented herself with a perfect Miss America image. Her clothing was feminine and conservative and she wore her hair elegantly upswept in classically feminine style. But *after* she won, I watched Leanza experiment with other images. When we appeared together on *The Joan Rivers Show*, she exuded a sporty image with a trendy navy pantsuit dotted with nautical medals and her hair worn in a short, casual fringed style. A month later, when she appeared on the cover of *Atlantic City* magazine under the headline "Miss America Gets Serious," she had switched to a conservative image with a pinstriped business suit and blunt-cut hairstyle. Each look was Leanza, but a side of her appropriate for *that situation*.

Frankly, she wouldn't have won if she'd used either of those looks at the pageant, but wisely, she cultivated and projected the look she needed to win the that specific title. Leanza understood the art of projecting the image of the pageant she hoped to win, while remaining herself. That's the secret. Don't change yourself. Use suitable hairstyles, makeup, and clothing to subtly reflect the pageant's image.

14 · Don't Be a "Clone"

While you should reflect the overall image of the pageant you enter, blatantly "cloning" the reigning queen or a previous winner can backfire.

A winner must achieve a *balance*, projecting the image of that pageant but also standing out from the crowd by being herself and being an original. "A winner is not a copy," asserts Kathleen Munson, adviser to Gretchen Carlson, the Miss America who won despite being everything that "couldn't win." "A winner is absolutely *not* a copy," she insists. A winner fits the image of the title she is seeking while *remaining an individual.* "Don't have preconceived ideas about winning or losing based on stereotypes. When Gretchen came to me, she said, 'Can I win? I'm five foot three and a hundred forty pounds.' But she *won.* Don't eliminate yourself from pageants because you're 'too short,' 'too fat,' you don't have the right 'look,' you don't have the right talent. Girls will say, 'But you have to be tall to win.' Look at Kelli McCarty, Miss USA 1991. She wasn't. Look at Gretchen. She wasn't. Or they'll say, 'But you have to have a talent in the traditional performing arts.' Look at Kaye Lani (Rafko). Her Tahitian dancing wasn't the typical dance performance. But she won. You have to break those stereotypes. Sure there's a definite *image* for each pageant. But a winner is not a copy! A winner is absolutely not a copy."

Unfortunately, contestants who lack self-confidence are afraid to be themselves and instead try to repeat a past winner's success by cloning her. What they fail to understand is that judges find such "sales pitch" images annoying. "You have to look through her eyes and ask, 'Can this woman stand in her own name—or is she trying to be someone else?'" says Richard Guy, who coached six women to the Miss USA throne, and now runs GuyRex's Miss United States. "Is she trying to copy last year's winner? If she's copying, I don't want her. I don't want a copycat!"

While each pageant does have a certain overall image, *there is no one exact "winning look" that is guaranteed to succeed*. Each pageant's image is a *general* quality. Once a contestant understands the general image of the pageant, she can—and should—display a great degree of individuality. "I bet if you asked the judges what they look for, they'd say something different each time," says Kaye Lani Rae Rafko, "because none of us are exactly the same. We may have similar qualities—but each girl is unique."

15 · Create a Winning Image

Nothing is more crucial to a young woman's chances of winning than *looking* like a winner. And winning images are *created*. "Think of yourself as a canvas," advises pageant clothier Thomas Tolbert, of Legends. "We are going to paint a masterpiece. You're telling me about yourself." To create an effective image, the girl has to understand not only the pageant she is entering, but who she is and what she wants her image to "say" to judges. He explains, "You've got to go *in* and find what is *inside*—their brains, their emotions. That's what is going to help me to dress them correctly and let the judges know who they are before they ever speak one word."

Creating an effective image is a matter of finding the right "theme" for the young woman. Is she a vivacious southern belle like Phyllis George or Mary Ann Mobley? Is she a smart, no-nonsense personality like Diane Sawyer or Leanza Cornett? "You're creating an image all the way through and you need to stick with it," explains Debbie Brown, a pageant clothier who dressed Miss America 1994 and Miss USA 1994. "The main thing when you're creating an image is to *be* your personality." Debbie offers an example: "Suppose that from the interview, the judges know that you're very intelligent, your personality is reserved, and your talent is opera. Then you come out in the evening gown competition wearing a slinky, low-cut, hot-red gown that Gypsy Rose Lee would wear. The judges are going to be confused and wonder, 'Is this girl real, or is she putting on a show because she wants us to *think* she's like this?'" If a girl's image contradicts her personality, says Brown, "It leaves you hanging like you don't know who she is." The image you create with your clothing, hairstyle, cosmetics, and carriage should instantly tell the judges who you are. Or, as David Bartley puts it, "Does your image match your message?"

A young woman's image should not only "match" her personal style, it should also present her at her finest. "People sell themselves short by not looking their best," says Bartley. "Like it or not, fair or not, that's life. There is a direct correlation between what you look like and your success. I'm sorry, but that's just the way it is. It doesn't mean you have to be the most gorgeous person. It means that you're the *best version* of you, that you have taken the time and effort to make yourself look your best."

A recent example of how much image can improve a contestant's chances is Lu Parker, Miss USA 1994. I compared her appearance minus make-up and with her thick hair let down in television's *Secrets Revealed* and in her state program book, against her appearance at the Miss USA Pageant. Talk about improvements. I hope she'll forgive me for saying so, but I never could have picked her from either as the next Miss USA. She had the winning figure, personality, and intelligence right along—but a better image, improved hairstyle, and makeup, helped the rest of us to *see* the champion in a champion.

Ultimately, the development of a winning image is one of the most valuable rewards of the pageant experience. "Whether or not they win the title, the self-improvement they receive is worth it," asserts Thomas Tolbert. "Everybody says, 'We're going for the crown.' Yes, I believe they *are* all going for the crown— but it's also a growing process. Getting to know yourself, to improve yourself—that's all part of the whole 'package.'"

Develop a winning image for pageants—and life.

16 · Know the Seven Winning Hairstyles

Like every aspect of a contestant's appearance, her hairstyle can make or break her image. The right hairstyle must be both the most flattering style for that young woman and a look appropriate for the pageant she is entering. "There is a winning look," says Peggy White, a respected Michigan hairstylist who created Kaye Lani Rae Rafko's winning coiffure. "It's not a hairstyle— it's a 'look.' It's feminine, natural, flowing, and right for the girl. It depends on her features and her look. The hairstyle should bring out the best in *her* features."

While every contestant should wear the hairstyle that most flatters her, it's helpful to know the seven basic hairstyles that are statistically most successful in pageants: long glamorous hair; long hair worn down with the crown pinned back; a long layered look; softly curled shorter styles; the sleek chignon; softly upswept styles; and a straight, shoulder-length cut. Each style conveys a specific image: sexy, elegant, or wholesome, as the case may be.

Although each of these looks has won in major pageants, some styles work better in one system than another because of a particular pageant's specific image. For example, long, thick, sexy hair is *the* winning look at Miss USA and Miss Universe— yet no one has become Miss America with below-the-shoulder hair in twenty years! Different hairstyles create very *different* images, just as a strapless red-sequin gown creates a quite different image than a flowing white chiffon gown.

To select your perfect hairstyle for competition:

- Study the hairstyles that have won.
- Know the image of the pageant.
- Find what flatters your facial shape.
- Learn what works for your hair texture.
- Consider how your hair "behaves" in the climate. (humid, dry) where the pageant will be held.
- Test what styles look best with your gown, swimwear, interview outfit, and costume.

Seven Styles for Success

The Layered-Look: Since Farrah Fawcett soared to fame in the 1970s, modified layered styles have been popular in every pageant, although sometimes in a less-sexy, above-shoulder version. Consider the climate where the pageant will be held since long, layered hair can be unmanageable in humidity. This look works well for thick hair that holds a curl. Examples:

America's Junior Miss 1992	Miss America 1988
Miss T.E.E.N. 1990	Miss Teen of America 1987
Miss Teen-USA 1989	Miss America 1986

Shorter, Softly Curled Styles: Shorter, lightly layered, softly curled styles (above the shoulder) are most successful in the scholarship systems. This easy-care look works well for curly hair and the coarser hair texture of women of color, and is the frequent choice of on-the-go titleholders during their reigns. Examples:

Mrs. USA 1991	America's Junior Miss 1986
Miss Universe 1990	Miss America 1984
Miss America 1987	

Long and Glamorous: Long, glamorous hair is the most successful style in both Miss USA and Miss Universe, but below-the-shoulder hair doesn't fare as well at Miss America, since it tends to look too sexy. Miss Teen USA 1991, Janel Bishop, updated the look with a spiral curl. This style works best for thick, manageable hair. Examples:

Miss USA 1993	Miss 1992 World-America
Miss Teen USA 1993	Miss World 1991
Miss T.E.E.N. 1993	Miss USA 1990

Long Hair With Crown Anchored Back: Long hair cascading down the back with the crown pulled back and anchored with a barrette is a classically beautiful style that is appropriate for many pageant systems. Its pretty no-fuss look is ideal for teen pageants. This style works well for all hair types except very curly. Examples:

America's Junior Miss 1994	Miss T.E.E.N. 1992
Miss Teen of America 1994	Miss Teen USA 1992
Miss Teen of America 1993	Orange Bowl Queen 1991

Elegantly Upswept: Softly upswept styles, including the French twist, are very successful today and rarely go out of fashion. The look is less effective in teen pageants since it looks too mature. Upswept styles are effective for baby-fine hair that won't hold a set, or coarse hair that is unmanageable. Examples:

Miss America 1994	Mrs. USA 1993
Miss America 1993	Miss USA 1992
Miss Universe 1993	Miss Universe 1992

The Sleek Chignon: The sleek chignon is a classically beautiful look that is most successful in the Miss Universe system. Lu Parker, Miss USA 1994, updated the style with a sleek "tipsy-tail." This revealing style requires a pretty face and ears. The controlled chignon is an elegant, easy-to-manage style for coarse or thin hair. Several major winners pinned-on braided or curled hair pieces. Examples:

Miss Universe 1994   Miss America 1991
Miss USA 1994   Miss Universe 1991

Shoulder-length Straight: Another style that wins, although less often, is a straight, shoulder-length cut with the ends softly curled under, and light bangs. This clean-cut, easy-care look can help a contestant stand out among girls with fussier hairstyles. However, because it lacks glamour, it doesn't work as well in Miss America and Miss USA. Examples:

America's Junior Miss 1993   Miss Teen of America 1985
Miss Teen of America 1992   America's Junior Miss 1985
Miss World 1987   Miss World 1981

But which, if any, of these style is "right" for you? Debbie Brown, whose clients include Miss America 1994, Miss USA 1994, and 1993 America's National Teenager, advises, "Don't clone yourself. The secret is, if your hair looks pretty down, wear it down. If it looks pretty up, wear it up. Don't think that you have to wear your hair in a certain style just because everybody else does. Wear what looks great on *you*."

While seven hairstyles win more frequently than others, a superior candidate can win with almost any style. Teri Utley became Miss USA 1982 with a short haircut, almost unheard of in that system. Ursela Lawson, an African American, won Dream Girl USA 1987 wearing her hair in the ethnic braided style popularized by Bo Derek in the film *10*. If a new hairstyle is perfect for an otherwise superbly qualified contestant, she'll win and *make* it a winning style.

Just as the right hairstyle can improve a young woman's

appearance, hair color can also be effective. "Cosmetic hair-coloring techniques can make your face look longer, slimmer, or wider," explains Richard Cardone, a hair-color specialist and member of Clairol's Presidential Hair Colorists Council. "Hair color can be strategically placed to diminish bad features or bring out good features." He cites Kaye Lani Rae Rafko's reaction to his subtly highlighting her brunette hair with golden tones to accent her eyes. "Her first comment was, 'Oh my gosh, I see what you mean. My eyes look so bright!' The main thing is to keep it soft and make sure the hair coloring does you justice," says Cardone. "And *don't* attempt it yourself. If you're going after a big title, there's nothing worse than having orange streaks!"

And for the record, there is no one winning hair color. Hair colors win in roughly the same percentages as they are found in the population: brunettes, followed by blondes, then redheads.

17 · The Art of the Perfect Makeup

Long gone are the days when Mary Campbell, Miss America 1922, boasted, "I don't use cosmetics. I never have. I don't need them." Today, correct cosmetics can virtually transform a young woman from fine to fabulous. As I mentioned earlier, when *Secrets Revealed* cameras filmed Lu Parker, Miss USA 1994, minus her makeup, the stunning beauty queen looked like any other college kid. Yet, with the right cosmetics, Lu turned into a world-class beauty. With a little practice anyone can learn to use makeup to create a winning image.

First, keep in mind the *purpose* for pageant makeup. It is not theatrical makeup. Pageant makeup should make the young woman look pretty and fresh under stage lights for the *judges*. As Debra Maffett, now a TNN host, explains, "A lot of girls put on stage makeup as if they were putting it on for the person in the back row to see. The judges are in the *front* row—and they're the ones who select the winner. When I was onstage I just added a little to my regular makeup. I put on enough for the first row—the judges. For the final telecast, I put on a few individual eyelashes to enhance my eyes. The lighting onstage is very bright and hard so you have to find a way to "pop" your features out, but make it look natural."

For the private interviews, makeup should be more subtle than for the stage events. One of the most common mistakes I observe while judging is clownish makeup. "For the interview I always put my makeup on as natural as possible, but at the same time enhance myself," Debra explains. "The first three years in Texas [when she lost] I put on *tons* of makeup, false eyelashes, the whole bit. But by the time I was in Atlantic City I had learned what enhanced me . . . and what was too much. For my interview I wore real natural-looking shades of lipstick and looked as soft and natural as I could. Makeup should be something that enhances, but doesn't look like makeup."

Here are some guidelines offered by several experts:

- To avoid breakouts wear foundation your skin is used to, but wear more and in a darker shade. Blend the makeup down the neck to prevent a "line."
- For more coverage use pancake or cream foundation.
- Powder your entire face with loose translucent matte powder to avoid a shiny face onstage/on-camera.
- Never wear frosted cosmetics. Use only matte finishes for a natural look.
- For color depth on TV, go one shade brighter (not darker) with lipstick and blusher.
- Avoid bright, unnatural eye shadows like blue or green.
- Use dark eyeliner/pencil to widen or define eyes, soften the line with a cotton swab.
- Try combining heavy mascara and individual lash clusters.

- For contouring use off-whites (not white) and gray-browns.
- Blend all makeup carefully.
- Avoid vivid nail polish colors. They are distracting.

18 · *Is Your Voice Turning Off the Judges?*

An excellent voice is a true asset because it completes a woman's image and makes her *sound* like a winner. The vast majority of national and international winners have excellent speaking voices. They sound as beautiful as they look. Winners noted for their superb voices are famed television journalist Diane Sawyer (America's Junior Miss 1963), Miss America 1993 Leanza Cornett, and Miss Universes Michelle McLean and Margaret Gardiner.

Just as a wonderful voice can help create a winning image, a voice that is monotone, high-pitched, nasal, or childish can be a detriment, simply because a woman with a poor voice doesn't sound like a winner. In fact, a Gallup poll conducted by Dr. Lillian Glass, a vocal coach to celebrities and author of *Talk to Win*, revealed that if people don't like how you sound, 64 to 80 percent of them will tune you out . . . no matter how great your message.[1]

That was the case at a recent national pageant, where several women I had assumed would be top contenders fared poorly because their speaking voices were unpleasantly high-pitched and nasal. Since a titleholder spends her year *speaking, speaking, speaking*, judges simply can't visualize someone who sounds like Olive Oyl being effective. And if judges can't imagine a young woman as the winner, they're not going to award her the title.

Unfortunately, many young women don't realize that a voice *can* be improved with help from a speech or theater coach. "Speech therapy is wonderful," says Cheryl Prewitt Salem, who worked hard to improve her voice in order to win the 1980 Miss America title. "I went to the speech teacher at my university. It didn't cost me a thing. He volunteered a couple of hours a week to help me with my diction, intonation, and placement—not to help me lose who I was, but to change my voice enough that I was comfortable with it. You never want to change who you are but to be the best you can be."

In addition to working with experts, a girl can improve her voice by recording herself chatting on the phone or in another relaxed situation, study the tape of her voice, and work to make improvements. For example:

- You need air to speak well. Breathe.
- Speak at a moderate pace. Fast speakers sound nervous. Slow speakers sound boring.
- Enunciate the end of each word.
- Don't let your sentences fade out.
- Soften regional "twangs" (they sound too nasal).
- Don't end a sentence on a high note as if you were asking a question.
- Copy professional "voices" like Diane Sawyer.

Also avoid annoying verbal habits such as: "she's like" (she said), "he goes" (he said), "ya know," "I mean," "ta" (to), and "'scuse me?" (excuse me?). Dr. Glass's research revealed that such verbal habits irritate two-thirds of listeners. [2]

Don't sabotage your chances by turning off the judges with your voice. Speak like a winner.

19 · The Winning Smile

An attractive smile is another important quality in creating a winning image. "I think a smile is absolutely one of the strongest statements a contestant makes," says Dr. Jeffrey Garner, an expert in cosmetic dentistry. He cites a *Psychology Today* survey that found that the feature people most wanted to improve was their smile.

Will a bad smile harm a girl's chances? "Absolutely," he says. "I know it's a good way to *kill* your chances of winning pageants. Their smile needs to be the best it can be, especially with closeup head shots, one-on-one interview situations, or if they make it to national pageants where cameras are right up on their face."

The most common dental problems are yellowed, poorly shaped, crooked, or spaced teeth. "The simplest procedure we do is contouring of their natural teeth," explains Garner. "We can shape the enamel and contour the teeth so they have a nice, soft, feminine smile." Yellowed teeth can be whitened with dental bleaching techniques. "Everyone wants a nice, white smile," he says. "Basically there are two ways you can lighten teeth." One bleaching process is done in-office during repeated visits. "It's a good system to use if they need their teeth whitened very quickly." Another tooth-whitening system can be used at home with a custom mouthpiece that holds a bleaching agent. "They put it in and wear it every night while they sleep for about two weeks. That works very well and is one of the simplest ways to get a dazzling white smile."

Today's contestants don't have to rely upon braces to correct dental problems. "Most contestants who could benefit from orthodontics don't have the time," says Garner. "They can't wait years. They have to have it done *now*." Crooked teeth and spaces can be diminished with *cosmetic* dental procedures. "Usually gaps are corrected with a bonding procedure or with porcelain laminate veneers. If you had a person with a tiny space between her teeth, if it could be sculpted easily, then bonding might be the choice." A big plus, he says, is that "bonding can be done in one office visit."

A contestant with more complicated dental problems requires a different treatment. "If you had a patient who had multiple spaces, crooked teeth, a protruding tooth, or *multiple* problems, then porcelain laminate veneers might be the best option. Porcelain veneers require a laboratory procedure so it is a two-visit procedure."

Many technologies are available for correcting problem smiles. Although prices differ according to the area of the country, cosmetic dental procedures are a considerable investment, ranging from $450 to $1,200 to correct a single tooth.

Since the late 1980s, when high-tech cosmetic dental procedures became widely available, an attractive smile has become increasingly important in competition. Although I know of half-a-dozen women who won national and world titles despite less-than-perfect teeth, it is becoming rare to see top contestants with flawed smiles in today's competitions. Make a pretty smile a priority.

20 · Should You Improve on Mother Nature?

In their efforts to create a winning image some contestants surgically change their appearance. Since most pageants don't prohibit cosmetic surgery, such "improvements" have become increasingly common. One surgeon has publicly stated that he has performed surgery on nearly fifteen hundred contestants including four Miss Americas, three Miss USAs, two Miss Teen-USAs, and one Mrs. America.[3] The most common procedures are nose jobs, breast implants, and liposuction on the thighs. Other contestants have had breast reductions, tummy tucks, and chin implants.

There's no question that it's going on, but views on such surgical alterations differ. Some contestants feel it gives girls who have surgery an unfair competitive advantage since judges actually score contestants on the *proportions* of their figures. Girls who undergo such operations feel that since their futures depend on winning, they are entitled to do "whatever it takes."

Pageant officials express concern that entrants are surgically altering their bodies to win, but claim they can't police such procedures.

As with so many complex issues in society today, there are no simple answers to the cosmetic surgery dilemma. Yet one fact is obvious: Insecure contestants attempt to copy what wins. If features associated with cosmetic surgery repeatedly win, that's what contestants will copy. That's *not* to encourage readers to go under the knife. There are potential risks to cosmetic surgery that every contestant should know:

- Researchers claim that silicone breast implants are linked with health problems including autoimmune disease.[4]
- In 1991, a moratorium on silicone breast implants was declared. Saline implants continue to be used.
- Manufacturers of silicone implants have agreed to pay over $4 billion to women who say breast implants harmed their health.[5]
- Complications from breast augmentation can include infection, leakage, and hardening of breast tissue.[6]
- Breast implants can block breast tissue, potentially preventing detection of tumors during mammograms.[7]
- Risks from cosmetic surgery (including liposuction and nose jobs) include infection, scarring, reactions to anesthesia, and (although rare) death.[8,9]

Fortunately, natural alternatives to surgery can improve many figure flaws. "There are much cheaper ways to look good," says Sharon Turrentine, a certified physical fitness specialist who advises contestants to achieve their best figure through nutrition and exercise. "It's cheaper to go to a gym than it is to go have elective surgery and have people cut on your body."

In addition, padding and taping the bustline, simple procedures permitted in most pageants, allow contestants to enlarge their bustlines without expensive, permanent, and potentially dangerous "internal padding." The right style swimsuit, gown, and undergarments can also make significant improvements in how a young woman's figure looks onstage.

While padding prevents the need for breast augmentation, facial flaws such as a bulbous nose or receding chin, which cannot be hidden, can undermine a girl's self-esteem and limit her chances of winning. Corrective surgery for such facial flaws can be beneficial. Since being a titleholder is a high-profile public relations job, a fair test of the need for cosmetic surgery might be: "Would I need this surgery to be hired as a local TV news anchor?" If a young woman's appearance could limit her professionally, then a reasonable case could be made for correcting the problem feature.

Yet before considering *any* type of cosmetic surgery, contestants need to take a realistic look at what wins. Yes, many bionic beauties are on the runway. However, many other young women won major titles despite less-than-perfect faces and figures. Very small-busted winners have included Miss Americas 1978 and 1981; Miss Universes 1983, 1984, 1985, 1986, and 1988; and Miss USAs 1976, 1979, 1981. Miss USA 1993 and Miss Americas 1989, 1990, and 1991 had less-than-ideal thighs. Miss America 1991 and Miss Universe 1994 had larger noses. Miss America 1980 had scars from emergency-room stitches to repair her face and crushed leg after a near-fatal car accident. She never underwent cosmetic surgery.

One of the most enlightening remarks on "true" beauty I have heard came from Dr. Shirley Cothran Barret, Miss America 1975, who holds a doctorate in education. "I think it is scary when the emphasis is put on the physical rather than the inside. The year we had the Pageant's reunion, there were forty-four Miss Americas in attendance. With all sincerity and respect, as I looked around I thought, 'How many labels could I put on these people?' Maybe one or two of them were 'beautiful.' There were a lot of *striking* Miss Americas, *cute* Miss Americas, *intelligent* Miss Americas, *poised* Miss Americas." In other words, individuals. As the rainbow of diverse titleholders proves, being a major titleholder is not about "perfection." It is about being an outstanding *individual*.

I can't advise a contestant whether or not she should have cosmetic surgery, because there's no way to predict the personal tastes and insight of the people who will judge her. Each girl and her parents need to evaluate the pros and cons of cosmetic surgery and decide what is best for that young woman's health and lifelong goals.

21 · Stand Out From Your First Moment Onstage

You should look like a winner from the first moment you step onstage, because the judges' first impressions set the tone for the rest of the contest. Contestants are usually introduced onstage in the "Parade of Contestants" or "Parade of States," in either costumes, suits, or gowns. From your first moment onstage, project the message: "I'm gonna be a top contender so keep your eyes on me!"

Parade of Contestants

Most pageants introduce contestants, who are attired in suits or evening gowns during a "Parade of Contestants." However, other pageants differ from year to year, sometimes having girls wear a gown or suit of their choice, other times having a guest designer provide gowns. The Miss Teen of America program usually introduces contestants in patriotic red, white, or blue blazers or suits.

Whatever the format, wear a stunning outfit that makes you look like a million bucks and is *slightly* different from what other entrants will be wearing. For instance, during the contestants' introduction at the 1986 Miss America Pageant, Miss

Tennessee, Kellye Cash, stood out from the crowd of look-alike beaded gowns by wearing a simple black gown with a large white fabric "fan" across one side of her bodice. There was no way the judges could overlook her when the top ten were announced. She won the crown.

Similarly, when contestants wore suits during the opening number at the 1981 Miss America Pageant, the eventual winner, Elizabeth Ward, set herself apart from the crowd of "serious" businesslike suits by wearing an elegant, romantic black-velvet suit with a ruffled neckline that framed her beautiful face. She looked like the winner the moment she stepped onstage. The introduction of contestants provides an ideal opportunity to catch judges' attention by looking slightly different from one's rivals for the crown. There is a fine line between looking individual and looking *odd*. The idea is to create a *positive* impression.

Costumes

Many pageants, like Miss USA, Miss Teen-USA, and Miss Universe, stage an opening production number with contestants in full costume representative of their community, state, or country.

In teen pageants, costuming should be appropriate for the age. "It needs to be wholesome and youthful," advises Warren Alexander, whose Miss Teen of America program asks entrants to come up with costumes symbolizing a great achiever from their state. "We've had Snoopy, Miss Piggy, the Pillsbury Dough Boy, a giant butterfly, and a Hershey's Kiss in silver lamé. It can't be too sophisticated for a teenager. You have to *present* it too," he says, citing the state contestant who came as a pumping artificial heart with protruding tubes and flashing lights. "You have to present it in such a way to get the most out of that costume."

In beauty pageants like Miss USA or Miss Universe, where the emphasis is on show biz and *glamour*, instantly standing out in costume can give an entrant a competitive edge. Although a separate panel judges the costumes, the winner of the "Best Costume" award often moves on to the semi-finals. In 1993, Miss Kansas-USA won the Best Costume award as an elegant Native American chief, made the finals, and became second runner-up to Miss USA. When judges have fifty or more contestants walking out at them briskly, they don't have a lot of time to think. Impressions are made quickly. "Costumes don't count toward scores," observes Alexander, "but the judges have *seen* you onstage. That makes an impression. Any time [contestants] are in front of the judges they are making an impression . . . and judges are going to remember them."

Costuming should craft an eye-catching, winning image instantly. One Miss Universe, Trinidad's Janelle Commissiong, outclassed the competition in a metallic gown with nine-foot-tall "wings." Kenya Moore, Miss USA 1993, wore a white winter gown with a fur-trimmed hood to win her crown and went to Miss Universe as an elegant Statue of Liberty. The most successful pageant experts in the world, from Venezuela and Colombia, whose titleholders regularly make the finals at Miss Universe, help their girls to stand out with dramatic costumes, such as beautiful historical gowns or sexy Indian wear. Miss Venezuela 1994, a statuesque athlete, came as a warrior in skimpy gold metallic armor. She became second runner-up to Miss Universe.

The famous GuyRex team of Richard Guy and Rex Holt, the only people ever to "produce" five back-to-back Miss USAs, are masters of costume design. Their secret included packaging their girls as spectacular rhinestone cowgirls in second-skin body suits, cowboy hats, metallic high-heeled boots, gun holsters, and ostrich-feather chaps. No GuyRex girl ever got lost in the crowd! The secret to using the costume competition as a key to the crown is: Look like the winner from the first moment you step onstage.

In any pageant, make sure your costume image matches the pageant. A sexy costume at Miss Teen of America is a no-no. A sedate "great achiever" costume with no sex appeal would bomb at Miss USA. Match the image.

The Winning Interview

Interviews are where pageants are won . . . or lost.
DONNA AXUM, FORMER MISS AMERICA
AND NATIONAL PAGEANT JUDGE

To the casual observer, a pageant winner earns her title onstage before television cameras and millions of viewers. In reality, the battle for the crown is often won or lost in the privacy of the judges' interviews. Indeed, interviews are *so* important that a blunder or lackluster performance there can cost a previously promising candidate her shot at the crown. Gary Collins, former host of the Miss America Pageant, recalls, "One year we had a girl who had a top talent and looked wonderful, but she couldn't function in the interview so there was no question she wouldn't make the top ten."

Why are those personal conversations with the judges so important? Unlike onstage competitions, personal interviews are an "up close and personal" environment that reveal each contestant's personality, intelligence, confidence, communication skills, and how she would handle the public and press as the titleholder. Interviews are so significant that judges admit that a good interview can make them "watch for" a candidate in other events.

What Judges Look For

Although exact judging criteria will differ from pageant to pageant, judges consider many of the following qualities:

- first impressions
- appearance, attire, and grooming
- poise and grace
- voice, grammar, vocabulary
- personality, sincerity, charm, charisma
- intelligence
- wit and sense of humor
- individuality, ability to be herself
- confidence, commanding presence
- ability to think quickly and express opinions clearly
- general knowledge in many areas
- knowledge of her platform or volunteer service
- sense of values, strength of character
- direct, but tactful, answers—versus evasiveness
- courage of her convictions
- ability to fulfill the titleholder's responsibilities
- overall impression

PUTTING YOUR BEST FOOT FORWARD

One of the secrets to successful interviewing is recognizing that what you do before the interview is as important as the interview itself. The better the preparation the better the interview. Prepare like a winner beforehand to prove to the judges that you are their winner.

22 · It's a Job Interview . . . Be Prepared

Whether the pageant is Miss World, Miss USA, or America's Junior Miss, the title awarded is a coveted *job*. The winner will serve as a spokesperson for the pageant and its sponsors. She will travel extensively, meet the president; appear on talk shows; give press conferences; tape commercials; host fundraisers; converse with political and business leaders; and deliver countless speeches to schools, colleges, churches, civic, and political organizations. Since a national winner is transformed into a celebrity for a year—and often for a lifetime—competition for the title is intense and judges can afford to be selective about who they "hire."

The private interviews with the judges are the most important part of that "hiring" process. "I knew that if I wanted to be Miss America I had to score well in—if not win—the interview," Marjorie Vincent remarked shortly after being named Miss America 1991. "That was what I focused on because I felt that if the judges did not get to know me as a person and find out in the interview that I was the one who should be Miss America, than I would not stand a chance."

Remember, your pageant interview is one of the most important job interviews you will have in your lifetime, with the potential to change your life radically. With so much at stake, prepare like a champion. "You have to *prepare* yourself," asserts former Miss Mississippi, Mary Donnelly-Haskell. "You have to educate yourself about what is happening in your state, the United States, and the world. Prepare yourself because no matter how wonderful your personality is, if the judges ask you, 'What do you think of euthanasia?' and you answer, 'I don't think they're as lucky as youth in America,' . . . that's gonna do you in!"

In pageants, one point can separate the winner from the losers, so the well-prepared competitor has an advantage. "I felt confident about my interview," admits former Miss America Debbie Bryant-Berge, "and I think it was because I had prepared for it. I guess I went at it like somebody getting ready for a match. I was excited about being in the interview situation and I felt confident." The interview can clinch the crown—or end the dream. Prepare like a champion.

23 · Understand Different Types of Interviews

Pageant interviews can differ greatly depending upon the interview format used in a particular system. They include:

Panel Interviews

Many pageants, such as America's Junior Miss, Miss Teen of America, and Miss Teenage America, conduct "panel interviews" where each contestant is interviewed by an entire panel of judges. The contestant is introduced and seated alone facing three to twelve judges, usually seated behind a conference table. Demanding panel interviews reveal if a girl can think on her feet, or in this case, her *seat*. Panel interviews usually count for 25 to 30 percent of preliminary judging.

Individual Interviews

Many pageants, including Miss USA, Miss Teen USA, Miss Universe, Mrs. America, and Miss Teen All American, conduct individual interviews where contestants talk with one judge at a time. After judges are seated at individual tables in a large room, contestants are brought in for one-on-one conversations with each judge. As a contestant ends an interview with one judge, she moves on to the next judge's table until she has chatted with each judge privately. The format's advantage is its less-intimidating atmosphere. Such one-on-one interviews usually count for one-third of preliminary balloting.

Conference Interviews

The conference-style interview is a new format introduced in the Miss America program in 1993, valued at 30 percent of preliminary scoring. It resembles a press conference, with the contestant standing at a speaker's podium facing the judges (and a cameraman and television lights at state and national levels).

As in a press conference, the young woman makes an opening statement about herself and then fields questions from the panel.

Since each pageant's interview format focuses on the qualities that system is seeking in its winner, contestants need to understand the differences.

For instance, since Miss Teenage America travels the country as a spokesperson for teenagers and pageant sponsors, her public communication skills are crucial. "Miss Teenage America must be able to articulate well, represent teenagers at sponsoring companies, and carry on a conversation about what's going on with today's teenagers," explains spokesperson Lori Moore. As such, judges evaluate finalists for "poise and public-speaking ability" during a panel interview with experts on teenagers.

Miss America is recognized as a spokesperson for worthy causes ranging from AIDS education to preventing violence against women. Although she also mingles with the public constantly, the emphasis of her "year of service" is serving as a spokesperson for her official "platform." Marjorie Vincent spent her year addressing the tragedy of domestic violence, including speaking before state legislatures. Leanza Cornett achieved national recognition for her work on behalf of AIDS education. National and state titleholders give hundreds of speeches in a year, sometimes several speeches in one day. Thus, the program's press conference–style interviews replicate the demands of the winner's "year of service" and reveal which contestants possess the knowledge, confidence, and communication skills to fulfill that responsibility.

Other pageants want a titleholder who is a "people person" with a vivacious, outgoing personality. Miss USA, for instance, has to be able to chat with everyone from hospitalized children to the celebrities she greets while handing out trophies at the

People's Choice awards. The informal interviews help judges to see which contestants have that great rapport with people. "In Miss USA your interviews are one on one with each judge," says Kati Fish, Miss Arkansas-USA 1993. "So it's more of a casual *conversation*, 'Tell me about yourself, the things you like to do, your likes and dislikes. Tell me about you as a person.' As opposed to the Miss America system where it's, 'Tell me about your platform and your views on the world.' I found the Miss USA system to be more relaxed."

Those conversational interviews reflect the nature of Miss USA or Miss Teen USA's reception-circuit reign. "In the Miss USA system it's all celebrity judges," Kati explains. "Those celebrities may be famous, but they're not always personable or outgoing, so sometimes you have to carry the conversation. But that is exactly what Miss USA has to *do*, because she is around celebrities and she's got to be able to relate to them. You have to be a completely charming hostess no matter what!"

Whatever the format, the interview with judges is critical because it highlights the most important quality required of *any* titleholder during her reign—the ability to quickly create a positive impact everywhere she visits. David Bartley, a respected pageant photographer who has worked with dozens of state and national titleholders, explains, "The winner has to be a young woman who can *affect* people—someone who can get off a plane, walk in a room, light it up, leave the room, get on a plane, and go do it all again someplace else," he says. "That's what it's all about."

And that's what interviews are intended to *show*.

24 · Knowledge . . . Your Most Valuable Interview Tool

Pageant interviews are also intended to reveal if a contestant can *think*. Clear thinking requires knowledge, and mental organization to use that information. To prepare well for the interview process, a girl needs to become a bit of a "human filing cabinet." The first step is to get an idea of what judges are likely to *ask*:

- anything on your entry form/fact sheet
- yourself ("Tell us about yourself" or "Who *are* you?")
- reasons for entering the pageant
- what you want to achieve in life
- educational and career goals, current job
- hobbies, sports, and unusual interests
- your best and worst qualities
- biggest disappointments and accomplishments
- people you admire most and why
- family, friends, boyfriends
- talent and any special training
- travel experiences
- community involvement/what your town is known for
- favorite music, movies, books, foods, sports, etc.
- world affairs and issues
- current events and controversial issues
- geography that's in the news (Gaza Strip, Bosnia)
- people in the news (Who is . . .)
- politics and presidential campaigns

There is no way to predict everything about which judges might ask since every interview is different. "It really can vary," observes Melissa Aggeles, Miss Florida 1988 and a national semi-finalist. "Judges could ask you anything from your favorite color to what you think about the Moscow Summit. It depends on what kind of mood the judges are in, what they feel the minute they see you, how interesting your résumé is. It really varies."

Once you've anticipated possible lines of questioning, the second step is to begin collecting information to study the issues. That builds the base of knowledge a girl needs to draw upon when answering questions. A notebook listing personal tidbits such as her goals, school, travel, honors, hobbies and funniest moments, can help a new contestant get ideas for answering personal questions. Newspaper and magazine clippings are ideal for prepping for questions on politics and current events. "Read everything you can get your hands on!" advises veteran local pageant director Jeff Bell, "*Newsweek, People, USA Today*, newspapers. Read it, analyze it, and move on."

Pick a system for organizing your information and ideas. As Miss Florida, Aggeles used index cards with questions and answers listed on flip sides. "I came up with about four hundred," she says. "I figured that if I didn't know something in the interview, it didn't matter because I knew four hundred *other* things." Miss Ohio 1988, Sarah Evans, kept a notebook with subject headings on each page. "I wrote down exactly how I felt about each issue so I had already put my opinion into words," she explains. "Then, if I was asked about that in interview, I already had a train of thought going."

Whatever system you decide upon, collect information about topics judges are likely to bring up. Digest facts about each subject, develop opinions, and practice possible answers. Absorbing information on a wide variety of subjects strengthens a contestant's confidence and improves the quality of her interviews. "I think the more issues you think about and try to formulate ideas about, the more it helps you," explains Debbie Bryant-Berge. "Even if you're not *asked* about that, you have the sense of preparedness that you can handle any situation that could come along. Even if they only ask you, 'What are you majoring in at college?,' you'll think, 'Come on, give me *more*! I'm *ready* for ya'! So you don't worry about it, you're not nervous—and that comes across in the interview."

If you want to collect crowns . . . collect information!

25 · Be Ready to Discuss Anything on Your Résumé

Because pageant interviews are based to a large degree on contestants' fact sheets, be prepared to discuss every item you've listed. "The only thing judges know about you is what you put on that piece of paper," says Dr. Sandra Adamson Fryhofer, a former Miss Georgia. "I recommend that contestants bring a copy of their résumé to the pageant and look it over before the interview to remind themselves what they've put on it, because that's what they're going to be asked."

Being prepared to converse about any subject on your résumé can nudge a contestant toward the throne. The four personal subjects most likely to be brought up by judges are a contestant's platform (or community volunteerism), talent, education, and career goals. Failing to prepare for questions about these subjects can hurt an otherwise successful interview.

Consider the case of the student I once judged whose entry form stated she was majoring in environmental science and planned to work for the Florida Environmental Protection Agency. By coincidence, an environmental chemist was on the panel. During the environmental major's interview, the chemist asked her a give-away question, "How does Florida dispose of its trash?" Strangely, the girl was stunned by the question, stammered "Scuse me?," and was unable to name even one method of disposal or recycling. Ironically, I had driven past a smelly man-made mountain of trash on my way into town, a memorable example of Florida's "solution" to excess garbage . . . practically in the girl's backyard! Her ignorance of a subject directly related to her college major didn't ruin her chances, but she *knew* she had goofed and it hurt her confidence throughout the interview. Always be prepared to discuss subjects related to your college studies.

A serious contestant must be able to discuss subjects related to her intended profession. I was appalled by the lack of aware-ness of her field demonstrated by a pre-law major I once judged. Noting that she planned to follow in the footsteps of her father, a prominent attorney, I asked if she thought there ought to be caps on lawyer's fees in multimillion-dollar law-suits. To our shock, she dismissed the question without even *attempting* to offer an opinion: "I'm sorry, I don't know about that issue." Her ignorance of issues related to her intended pro-fession made her look inept and eliminated her from serious consideration. Ignorance of one's stated area of professional interest can be a costly blunder.

Being unable to discuss something on her résumé usually won't cost a girl the crown on the local level where judges are understanding, but it *will* undermine her confidence. "I'm not really critical, because the girl just may not have given it much thought," says Jeff Bell, who judges extensively on the local level where such oversights are most common. "But if an exag-geration happens to be pointed out, it can backfire on her and ruin her entire interview. She's not going to be able to think clearly for the rest of the interview because she's worried in *her* own mind: 'Ah, they caught me!' So, not only can it blow that one question," says Jeff. "It can ruin her whole interview."

A fact sheet can also prompt judges to ask a contestant about subjects she is knowledgeable about and can discuss with con-viction. A case in point is Kaye Lani Rae Rafko. When she com-peted at the nationals the judges were fascinated by an entry on her personal résumé: She was an oncology-hematology nurse who worked with cancer and AIDS patients and hoped to open a hospice center one day. When judges asked her about her pro-fession, Kay Lani spoke with passion about her terminal patients, the nursing profession, and the role of hospice care. Her interview scores were so high they elevated her to the crown.

26 · Talk, Talk, Talk!

Strong communication skills are one of the most effective keys to the crown. Since pageant interviews combine elements of both public speaking and casual conversation, a contestant should become skilled at both arts. To develop public speaking skills, contestants should practice speaking before an audience. "Speaking is a skill that is *learned*," says Donna Axum, a former Miss America and two-time Miss America judge. "I would suggest that every contestant take a course in extemporaneous speaking. There are courses offered in high school and at local colleges. Take as many courses in speech as you can because it trains you mentally to answer questions. If you can give a hundred speeches around your community—do it!" The more you speak in public the more confident you become communicating to your "audience" of judges during personal interviews (as well as onstage interviews with emcees).

Helping their titleholders become winning communicators through months of constant public speaking is one of the "secrets" of the famed GuyRex team, former owners of the Miss Texas-USA franchise that produced five back-to-back Miss USAs (1985 to 1989). Laura Martinez Herring, the first in that chain of champions, started off as a *shy* naturalized Mexican-American citizen with a thick accent. Within two years, she was chatting away with Bob Barker at the Miss Universe Pageant in front of 600 million viewers as the first Hispanic Miss USA. Observes Herring: "Making speeches really *does* something for you." Absolutely. It gives you the confidence and communication skills to convince the judges you're their winner.

Take every opportunity to improve your communication skills:

- Practice interviewing in front of a mirror.
- Take speech classes in school.

- Sign up for your school's debate team.
- Give speeches to local clubs and schools.
- Join a Toastmasters club.

Pleasant conversation skills are important in any pageant system. "It needs to be spontaneous," says Dennison Keller, noted official and judge. "There's a certain relaxation where the person is just chatting with you. There's got to be a genuine dialogue of give-and-take. Don't speak *at* the judges. Speak *with* them and *to* them."

Fortunately, friendly, relaxed conversational skills can be developed with a two-step strategy: Keep up with topics likely to come up in conversation, and constantly interact with people around you. "One of the main things you can do to speak more easily is to be *knowledgeable*," says Kati Fish, Miss Arkansas-USA 1993. "If you have no idea what's going on in the world you're *not* going to be able to speak easily to anyone about any subject. Know what's going on in the world around you!" Second, she says, "Force yourself to be around people, to create conversations, to talk to people. If you're standing in line in the grocery store, start a conversation with the person behind you. If you're in line for concert tickets, talk to the next person in line. That's the easiest way to become a more outgoing person."

Such practical steps have worked for many titleholders. Kris Beasley, Miss Tennessee 1986, practiced interviewing with her father every night. "He would ask me how I felt about different issues, and I would toss those issues around. He helped me to see sides of issues that I had never thought about before and to become more competent in expressing my thoughts. But in the beginning," she admits, "I was afraid to even answer in front of him because I was afraid I might not sound right. But I found that the more I spoke, the better I became, and the more I knew what to say. It got to the point where my father would say, 'Man, I never have to worry about what you're going to say because you always pull it off.' Experience is the best teacher."

As these winners prove, whether it is public speaking or conversation, the art of communication can be mastered by any girl willing to talk, talk, talk.

27 · Perfect Your Performance With Mock Interviews

While there are many ways to improve *general* communication skills, the most effective method of improving *interview technique* is through "mock interviews." Indeed, videotaped interviews have proven so useful that they are routinely used by pageant preparation committees to prepare state winners for national competition. A camcorder records the contestant as she is questioned by a panel of "pretend" judges. Reviewing the tape allows the young lady to detect unflattering mannerisms, facial expressions, or slang she had been unaware of. "It's important for them to know how they look," explains Vernon DeSear, who prepared numerous Miss Floridas for national competition. "The video can help them to see how they're coming across visually and to evaluate their strengths and weaknesses." By repeating the sessions regularly the young lady can monitor and improve her performance.

As Cheryl Prewitt Salem knows from experience, mock interviews are invaluable because they offer girls a "safe" place to iron out blunders *before* meeting the judges. "Being good in interview takes a lot of practice," she says. "Practice in front of a panel where you can't go, 'Oh shoot, I wish I hadn't said that.' With mock interviews you have to literally go from beginning to end. It helps a girl to be as prepared as she can possibly be."

Fortunately, any contestant can improve her skills with mock interviews in the privacy of her home:

• Borrow or rent a video camcorder if you don't already have one.

- Use family, friends, and neighbors as judges.
- Have a friend tape your entry, interview, and exit.
- Study each tape to find what you need to improve on (shaky voice, nervous mannerisms, weak answers).
- Work on improving those specific flaws.
- Repeat the process until you're satisfied.

Mock interview "rehearsals" are a key to successful interviewing. As Jeanne Swanner Robertson, a humorist and national judge, put it, "I would be very disappointed in the young woman of the nineties who would come to a pageant representing her state, but not take the time to sit with a group of people who'll ask her questions, and say, 'Let me see if I can answer these.' That's just good common sense. It's a waste of her time and energy not to be ready when she comes in." Practice, practice, practice!

28 · Be Prepared for Anything

Interviews can be full of surprises, so be prepared for anything! Judges' personalities can affect the "feel" of an interview, making it anything from challenging and serious to relaxed and fun. Be flexible, because the one quality every winner needs is the ability to be friendly, comfortable, and confident with any person in any situation. If the judges steer the interview toward serious subjects to see if you're intelligent, give them what they want. If they bring a light tone to the interview to see if you have personality, adjust to that mood. Learn to establish rapport with *any* judge in *any* environment.

Never get "frozen" into one interviewing style. An attorney and former national runner-up told me off the record that not being taught to handle different judging styles ruined her chances:

"When I was at the state level they had judges who had been at it for years and they asked me about political issues which I was a pro at answering. When they asked me about capital punishment, I went over the history of Supreme Court decisions. When they asked me about fuel prices I quoted to them from Milton Freedman. It was great. I was so prepped for these tough political questions. Then I got to Atlantic City where the judges were asking things like, 'Why did you pick that color nail polish?' and 'If the man you were dating turned out to be married what would you do?' I almost fell off my chair! I was prepped for these tough grilling sessions . . . and it didn't happen. I blew it because I had no sense of humor. If somebody had just said, 'You know they might ask you silly questions, so remember to be spontaneous.' When the first runner-up was asked what she'd do if her boyfriend turned out to be married, she joked, 'I'd shoot him!' That's what they wanted to hear."

As this young woman learned too late: Be prepared for anything and give the judges what they want. "This is not an oral test!" quips speech and drama instructor Warren Alexander. "It's a *conversation*."

Being able to adapt to differing types of interviews comes down to developing the ability to "connect" with all kinds of people. "You need to bridge that gap between yourself and the judges," explains Kristin Huffman, Miss Ohio and fourth runner-up to Miss America 1990. "It's meeting people on their own level. You need to walk in there thinking, 'Okay, I want to get to know these people. I want them to know that I'm ready to meet them on their level.'"

Because any type of interview can be unpredictable, be prepared for anything and ready to radiate personality and confidence in all situations.

29 · Show Them You're Smart

Today's pageant winners have to have *brains*. Whether she seeks the title of Miss T.E.E.N. or Miss Universe, a major titleholder's job involves press conferences and interviews, talk shows, appearances for corporate sponsors, and countless speeches, sometimes before state legislatures and congressional subcommittees.

Judges know that, whatever the title, their winner has to be able to capably express her views on complex issues. "I look for an intelligent young woman who is vitally interested in what is going on in the world around her, an articulate young woman who has something to say about the issues," says Donna Axum. "This is not a memorized surface answer, but a digestion of the issue, an understanding of the problem, and an answer that reflects her opinion on that issue based upon her beliefs and values."

Interestingly, in recent years all major pageant systems have expected their titleholders to be intelligent young women whose education, knowledge, and accomplishments reflect well upon the pageant. Consider recent Miss Americas. Gretchen Carlson (1989) was an honors student at Stanford and Oxford, Debbye Turner (1990) was earning her doctorate in veterinary medicine, and Marjorie Vincent (1991) was a law student at Duke University.

Even in the Miss USA Pageant, unashamedly a "beauty pageant," recent winners have been increasingly well-educated women. Miss USA 1994, Lu Parker, was a master's degree recipient from the Citadel and founder of H.A.T.S., Help All Teens Survive. "The girls are glamorous and beautiful, yet they have so much more going for them!" explains Paula Miles, Parker's state director. "For instance, Lu certainly had a *purpose*. Now that's not a requirement to be in the pageant, but it gave her something to focus on and be knowledgeable about, and to appear intelligent and worldly." As Lu Parker discovered, it pays to show them you're smart.

The accomplishments of many titleholders at the time they won demonstrate that brains pay off in pageants:

- Miss World 1991—industrial engineering major
- Mrs. USA 1991—Ph.D. in Psychology
- Miss Universe 1981—engineering student
- Miss Nebraska-USA 1992—emergency room doctor
- Miss Iowa-USA 1993—medical doctor
- Miss America 1975—masters degree in education
- Miss South Carolina 1992—medical doctor
- Miss USA 1992—Attended Pepperdine University on an academic scholarship

30 · The Power of Personality

Intelligence is important. But intelligence alone won't capture the crown. No matter how bright and knowledgeable a candidate for the crown is, she must be an outgoing "people-person" with the ability to positively affect people from all walks of life. Without that quality, a girl might as well toss away her banner and go home. "She has to be confident, sincere, and have a congenial personality," asserts Warren Alexander, national director of the Miss Teen of America Pageant. "I expect to get phone calls, letters, and feedback from charities, businesses, and schools saying, "We were so impressed by this young lady! She touched people, she made a difference. We'd love to have her come back.' That's what I expect and that's what I tell my judges. She has to be someone who doesn't just compete well—because she is not going to be competing for the next year. She's going to be making *appearances* for a year. She has got to be a young lady who truly is tops."

Every contestant needs to know that national and world titleholders are not cool, reserved, composed little china dolls. They have personality-plus. I know dozens of such winners, and they are the nicest, friendliest, funniest, most charming people you could ever hope to meet.

From my vantage point, knowing so many of these vivacious

women, when I've faced cautious, "poised" contestants in interviews, the contrast has been glaring. Some contestants, even those whose photos and résumés indicated they might be top contenders, had no personality in the interview. It was as if they were concentrating so hard on being whatever somebody has told them they were "supposed" to be in interview, that they forgot to let their personality show. Interview is not the time to turn down the voltage on your personality. It's the perfect time to let the judges see the mega-watts "sparkle" you would bring to the crown. Shine!

The reason it's so important to let your personality show is because it's one quality that can't be faked. "You cannot coach or give that quality of charisma," states Kathleen Munson, a pageant consultant who has worked with numerous titleholders including Gretchen Carlson, Miss America 1989. "I don't believe charisma is a coachable quality. You can do a lot, but you can't give them that." A girl can undergo cosmetic surgery to win swimsuit. She can take talent lessons to cop the talent trophy. She can create the illusion of beauty with an expensive stylist and makeup artist, and a designer gown. But she cannot fake sincerity, charm, warmth, wit, compassion, and all the other intangible qualities that give a young woman that wonderful winning quality called "personality."

Personality is the character of a queen, the mark of a successful interview, and a contestant's greatest asset in pageants. If you achieve nothing else in your interview, make sure you use the power of personality.

31 · Learn to Manage Nervousness

Like competing in the Olympics, facing a panel of celebrity pageant judges whose scores on your "performance" could change the course of your life is an understandably nerve-wracking experience. It's a one-shot deal and you've got minutes to win the panel over. Indeed, *not* being nervous would be the real surprise.

The pressures of upper-level competition can be especially tough on contestants' confidence. "It can be very intense," says Debbie Bryant-Berge, a former Miss America and past Miss America telecast commentator. "A lot of people go into pageants and they are so tense because they want to do well, but they're so nervous that it affects their performance."

The most effective way to conquer such point-losing jitters is to prepare beforehand. "In the interview, when you see five or ten judges lined up against the other side of the table and you're sitting there by yourself—the situation *is* intimidating," says Christi Taunton, a former Miss Arkansas. "But if you are *prepared* when you get there, you really shouldn't have much of a problem with nervousness. I think preparedness is the greatest thing you can do to block the nerves."

Keep in mind that judges are real people. Like anybody else, they work long hours, get the flu, and have car trouble. "The girls need to realize that judges are people who put their shoes on every morning and brush their teeth just like they do," says Jeff Bell, a longtime local pageant director. "I think that helps the girls feel more relaxed." And if all the above doesn't help, he suggests this unique strategy: "Picture them in their underwear!"

So when you're hit with the shakes, sweaty palms, and rapid breathing, remember to relax and treat the judges as regular folks. "We have as much stress as we put on ourselves," asserts Lee Beaman, Miss North Carolina 1988. "It's a matter of keeping the interview in perspective. It's just a conversation with people. They mess up and make mistakes, they're not perfect, and they know that we're not. This will be your one moment in the spotlight. Why be nervous? Let it be fun! If you have your mental attitude right, it's usually not too stressful."

CREATE A WINNING INTERVIEW IMAGE

Feeling confident during the judges' interview is easier when a young woman knows she looks her best. Psychologists tell us that being well dressed and groomed not only increases the wearer's confidence, it elicits a more favorable response from others. To help judges see you as their winner, strive to create a winning image with your clothing and body language.

32 · Dress to Win

Pageants are a competitive situation similar to a job interview. And as with any important employment interview, a contestant should dress for success. "You are interviewing for a $150,000-a-year job," asserts Robin Elliott-Bear, of Robin Elliott Ltd., pageant clothiers. "I try to keep that in mind (while wardrobing) from the local-to-national level. Starting at the local level, judges are looking for a girl who could be the next Miss America. So it's just as important at the local level as it is at the state level—which a lot of young ladies forget. Whatever level they are in, I try to find the outfit that makes them look as if they *could* walk away with the national crown."

The most important part of that image is the reaction it creates *instantly*. Research shows that when people are introduced, their first impressions become lasting impressions. In pageants, instant reactions are viewed as so significant that "first impression" is an actual judging criterion in many systems. "That first impression is a lasting one," says Robert Zettler, past president of the Miss Ohio Pageant, "and when you're making a judgment at the end, it *is* going to come into play." From the first moment judges meet an entrant, her clothing should create the image of a winner.

Since every pageant has its own image, clothing must be

(IRV KAAR)

Scholarship pageants require a career look for interview.
Debbye Turner, Miss America 1990, chose a sophisticated
suede ensemble.

appropriate for the pageant system. "There's a difference, so
you need to know the system you're dealing with," explains
Kathleen Munson, owner of The Pageant Shop. "You have to
ask yourself, 'What am I interviewing for?' In the Miss USA
system, you are interviewing for a glamorous job. In the Miss

(THE PAGEANT SHOP)

In true "beauty" pageants, more glamorous styles and
shorter hemlines are acceptable.

USA system interviews are very 'cocktaily,' even at the teen
level. In the Miss America system, you're interviewing for a
scholarship program. It's a career look. You don't interview for
'scholarship and career' in a cocktail dress. Many of the teen
pageants, like Miss T.E.E.N., have a Miss America feel. Ask

yourself what that system is all about, then figure out what is appropriate."

The format of the interview also affects clothing choices. Since interviews require confidence and concentration, a contestant cannot afford the distraction of needing to adjust uncomfortable clothing. "I have them do the 'sit test,'" explains Elliott-Bear. "Nothing is worse than an outfit that doesn't 'sit' well. Sometimes when you sit, an outfit will pop in the center and make you look like you have a big bubble at the waist. Usually a two-piece works better. Also stay away from linens and other fabrics that wrinkle easily. That's one reason we picked a knit for Marjorie Vincent [Miss America 1991]. It just held up so well."

The girl's personal style is another consideration. "It's important to find the wardrobe that best suits that person's personality," explains Robin. "If they are a powerful personality, you try to keep that going throughout. Marjorie Vincent is a very powerful speaker, so she needs to wear reds and brights when she speaks. I did her [national] interview outfit, which was a red knit with a black asymmetrical scarf from her shoulder to her right hip. The look was feminine but still corporate, very powerful, and it worked with her attitude and image. The wardrobe should suit the image of the person."

As Marjorie's outfit illustrates, color can be used to reflect or create image. (See Tip #88, "Use 'Color Psychology' to Convey Image.") "If she is very demure, very young, she needs a pastel color," explains pageant wardrobe specialist, Thomas Tolbert, of Legends. "I'll put her in a pastel, a peach or pink, or an ivory or white suit. Now if she has a mild interview, but she's wearing a red suit, I'm going to be disappointed because red is a very vibrant color that gets you emotionally excited. But if a girl is really intense and she walks in wearing a red suit, then I'm going to say, 'Wow . . . here she is!'" Mismatched

(ROBIN ELLIOT, LTD.)

Miss America 1991, Marjorie Vincent, proved that an elegant
dress can be a winning alternative to an interview suit.

images can confuse the judges. "If they're climbing over the table to get their point across, but they're in lace silk," says Tolbert, chuckling, "it just doesn't work. I tell everyone, 'Think of yourself as a canvas. You're telling me about yourself.'"

Interview attire should always be flattering, age-appropriate, and well accessorized. "You want an interview suit to contour your body," says Kathleen Munson. "You're not looking for a 'mother-of-the-bride' look. You want it to shape your figure somewhat. It can be a one-piece or two-piece. Choose four-season fabrics:

(LEGENDS)

A feminine, fitted suit with a shorter skirt is a popular choice with contestants.

crepe, featherweight wool, a lightweight knit. The neckline should take your face shape into consideration. Analyze your face shape, then decide on your neckline. You want an age-appropriate hemline. With teens a short hemline is appropriate," Kathleen advises, but contestants in conservative pageants or competitions for married women may prefer more modest skirt lengths. "Finish is everything," she continues. "I don't care if you've got a hundred-dollar suit or a fifteen-hundred-dollar suit, you've got to finish with appropriate earrings and nice shoes."

Your interview attire "defines" who you are for judges. Make sure your clothing makes you look and feel like a winner.

33 · Don't Become a "Clothing Casualty"

While the right clothes can help clinch the crown, the *wrong* attire can damage a contestant's chances by causing judges to question her judgment. (If she'd wear *that* in an important competition, what would she be likely to wear in public as the winner?)

Just such a situation occurred recently when a top contender for a national title wore large crystal earrings and a rhinestone-dotted cocktail dress to a morning pageant interview. Etiquette dictates that one not wear cocktail attire in the morning—let alone to a be interviewed for a $150,000-a-year job. Her inappropriate choice of clothing was so jarring to judges that it became an obstacle she had to surmount to win us over. (During private deliberations later, one judge admitted, "To me she had to overcome her outfit.") Fortunately, despite the blunder, the contestant was superb throughout the pageant and went on to become a top runner-up. But, who can say whether she might have won had she *looked the part* during the private interviews when we judges were forming our first impressions of each woman's suitability for the crown?

Clothing mistakes can be costly. One national contestant ruined her chances by wearing flimsy underwear. Rather than focusing on her answers, judges were distracted by the sight of her nipples jutting through her sheer bra and knit dress! Another contestant wore a short skirt that she had failed to put through the crucial "sit test." Throughout her interview the panel was distracted by a splendid view of her undies! When she left the room, a judge quipped, "I made a note to tell her how nicely her panties matched her outfit." Such clothing mistakes cause judges to conclude that the young woman lacks good judgment and would make similar mistakes in public as the titleholder. In other words, clothing blunders can cost you the crown.

Avoid:

- garish colors and too-trendy fashions
- dyed satin shoes, flats, too-high heels
- swaying earrings/noisy bracelets
- low-cut necklines and see-through fabrics
- revealing "natural-look" bras
- too-short skirts
- "loud" hosiery
- purses carried into the interview

Select attire that creates the image of a lovely, tasteful young woman qualified to represent her community, state, or nation. Dress like a winner.

34 · Use Winning Body Language

From the moment a contestant enters the room to be interviewed, judges scrutinize her, asking themselves, "Does this young lady have what it takes to be our winner?"

How the candidate performs in those first moments is critical. "What kind of impact does she make on me visually when she walks in that door?" asks Donna Axum, who judges extensively on the state and national levels. "Is she genuine? Can I see her heart through her eyes?" A woman possessing the confidence and outgoing personality to reign as a titleholder immediately radiates those qualities to the panel.

When you make your entrance, remember:

- Smile! Your face sets the tone for the judges.
- Make eye contact with the judges immediately.
- Let your walk convey both grace and energy.
- Greet the judge(s) enthusiastically.
- Take your position (seated or standing) gracefully.

- Keep smiling, but in a natural, friendly manner.
- Discreetly take a deep breath before answering.
- And have fun!

A contestant must also demonstrate the body language of a winner throughout her interview to convince judges she *is* their winner. Few girls understand that in any life situation, a "grading" process takes place subconsciously whenever people are introduced. The mind mentally picks up on subtle nonverbal "clues" that reveal how a person feels about herself: posture, walk, seated position, level of energy, eye contact, facial expressions, and hand gestures. Negative body language such as slumped posture, poor eye contact, a wilted handshake, an uncertain voice, or nervous mannerisms like drumming fingers or kicking one foot, indicates low self-esteem. Body language can also reveal temperament: Is she confident or timid, introverted or extroverted, high-strung or placid?

Judges, who are usually pros at "reading" people, realize that such "body language" will speak volumes about how each girl would function as the titleholder. As a result, they can often sum up a contestant as a "potential winner" or "noncontender" based to a large degree on nonverbal communication. In other words, judges have a gut opinion about her chances of winning even before she utters a word!

Fortunately, the "wrong" body language can be corrected with awareness and practice. Compare examples of body language:

Don't	Do
look nervous/too serious	smile frequently
dart eyes around the room	maintain steady eye contact
twist rings/pick fingernails	rest hands calmly in lap
kick foot nervously	keep feet together and still
cross arms across chest	keep arms by sides, hands in lap

clench fists	keep hands open and relaxed
slouch/lean back in chair	sit erect and confident
cross legs at knee	cross legs at ankle
point a finger at judges	use upturned palm to gesture

Nonverbal communication has the power to instantly "tell" judges "I'm your titleholder." Rod McKuen, a judge for the 1982 Miss America Pageant, was skeptical that body language could reveal their eventual winner . . . until Debra Maffett walked in the interview room. "The first time I saw Miss California, I *knew* she was Miss America," he later admitted. "There was a way she walked—it was almost even before she spoke. I couldn't believe it. I thought, 'Holy smoke!' There was a certain amount of assurance she seemed to radiate."[1]

That commanding presence is an actual judging criteria and the recognized "sign" of a winner. "We tell our judges, 'Look, when the girl walks in the room, she could be wearing a paper bag and make an impression,'" explains Warren Alexander, of Miss Teen of America. "Does she command your attention? Does she get your respect? Does she *present* herself physically before she even speaks, in a manner that suggests, yes, this indeed could be our titleholder?" A winner's body language makes her stand out the moment she enters a room.

Body language can make or break a contestant's image. Understand how judges "read" nonverbal communication and make sure your body language sends one message: I'm a winner!

WINNING INTERVIEW STRATEGIES

Interviewing is an art. Knowing and using the right strategies during conversations with the judges can mean the difference between winning or losing. Know the strategies for success.

35 · *Know Your Judges and Headlines*

Be forewarned. Before entering an interview, there are two things every contestant should know: her judges and the day's headlines.

A favorite judging technique for testing contestants' mental alertness is to ask, "Who is so-and-so?" using another *judge* as "bait." The question sorts the intelligent from the inept. At one state pageant a member of the panel asked an entrant, "Do you know who Joe Sanders is?" When the girl nodded confidently, the judges assumed that she would reply, "Yes, Joe Sanders is a judge here and president of the Miss South Carolina pageant." To their amusement, she answered with complete confidence, "Yes, I do. Joe Sanders is a famous major league ball player. In fact, he was just traded to another team, but I'm not sure which one." With Sanders sitting in their midst, the judges could barely keep straight faces. The moment the contestant left the room they nearly fell off their chairs laughing. The stunt has been pulled at pageants from coast to coast, so be prepared. Learn who your judges are and memorize their names.

Another little surprise judges often pull is asking something from the morning paper. Kim Boyce, a 1983 Miss America semi-finalist recalls: "The morning of my interview, the girl who was helping me get ready was reading to me while I was putting my makeup on, and she read me an article. Well, I went into the interview—and sure enough, *that's* what they asked me about. If she hadn't been reading me the paper I wouldn't have had anything to say." Get the news that morning, even if it's just listening to the TV as you're rolling your hair.

Checking out the morning news can give a contestant a competitive edge, as Leanza Cornett demonstrated during her national judges interview. As she discussed her platform on AIDS education, Leanza slipped in the news that a famous film star had died from AIDS that morning. One judge, a prominent

Hollywood casting director, gasped in shock and entreated Miss Florida for more details. The incident revealed Leanza as a smart cookie who understood the power of being one headline ahead of the competition. Her attention to detail in preparing to meet the national panel distinguished her as a woman who put in extra effort to get the job done right.

Be prepared. Know your headlines and judges.

36 · Keep Your Composure

In any competitive situation the unexpected can occur: a contestant trips walking in the room, knocks over the stand microphone as she sits down, or calls a judge by the wrong name. Because mishaps do happen on any level of competition, remember that no disaster is so calamitous that you can't handle it with poise. Always keep your composure. When the unexpected occurs, turn it to your advantage with honesty, humor, or wit.

Kenn Berry, a Miss New York regional director and state and national judge, cites the case of a state contestant whose ring snagged and tore her hosiery during her interview. Since the judges had observed the mishap, the young lady slapped her hand over the run in mock horror and quipped, "Darn it, there goes my interview!" Says Berry, "I appreciated that because she was being totally honest. She reacted to it the right way and when she walked out of that interview, I gave her the highest score I gave any girl in that pageant because she was honest under fire. Those things impress me as a judge."

Should the unexpected occur, turn the incident to your advantage by keeping your composure and handling it in a relaxed, down-to-earth manner.

37 · Get to the Point

Get to the point. Rambling is a sure sign that a contestant hasn't prepared adequately. When a girl hasn't mentally digested an issue, her thoughts are disorganized and she has difficulty putting her views into words. She bluffs, hoping her rambling sentences add up to a solid answer. Instead, she's hanging herself on a verbal noose.

Rambling reveals a girl's inability to think clearly and saps energy from her interview by slowing the rate of questioning. The surest sign of a poor interview is how it "drags." By comparison, a top contender immediately stands out because of her ability to state her opinion concisely and move on to the next question. The result is a breezy, highly energized interview. The most successful interviews in national competition are so wonderfully fast-paced and energetic that we judges find ourselves stumbling over each other to squeeze in another question.

"Learn to speak precisely," advises Cheryl Prewitt Salem. "Get to the point of what you want to say and *shut up*. You're talking only seven minutes. You don't have *time* to ramble on. Learn to think: 'One . . . two . . . three . . . and shut up. One . . . two . . . three . . . and shut up.'"

Consider this fine straight-to-the-point answer given by a national semi-finalist and law school student. "Do you think the United States should assassinate Saddam Hussein," I asked her. "No," she replied without hesitation. "I don't believe the United States government should violate international law to assassinate leaders of other nations." A western contestant with an earthier, shoot-from-the-lip style simply quipped, "Of course!" Compact answers require clear thinking. Train yourself to analyze a question quickly, pick out the main point, and state your opinion clearly and concisely.

One interview habit that prevents a young lady from getting to the point effectively is repeating the judge's question. Although entrants are sometimes advised to do so to gain time to think, most judges are irritated by the practice. Kenn Berry admits that contestants who repeat his questions "drive me up a wall." He offers an example. "If I ask her, 'Do you think women are better equipped to handle loneliness than men?,' she'll go, 'Do youuuu think women are better eeequippped to handle loneliness thaaaan men?' I *know* she is stalling for time and that rubs me the wrong way. I don't want the girl to repeat the question to me. I want her to *answer* it."

Instead of wasting time and annoying judges, use a brief pause instead. Pausing to think before speaking is far more effective than repeating the question to buy time. It allows a moment to get the general idea of what you want to say *before* answering. That prevents point-losing rambling and helps prevent blunders. To make your interview answers all they can be, pause to think before you speak, and get right to the point.

One . . . two . . . three . . . and shut up!

38 · Add a Dash of Humor

Humor is an invaluable tool for contestants. The ability to make judges laugh can make a girl appear more confident, personable, and intelligent, and energize even the dullest interview.

For instance, John Moskal, a state and national judge and former costar on *Days of Our Lives* and *Remington Steele*, recalls a time when humor transformed a "stone-face serious" interview into a fun, high-scoring interview. "This girl was so *serious* that when it was my turn to ask a question, I said, 'Susie, can you complete this statement? You guys would just die if you knew that I . . .'" The question brought a smile to the contestant's face as she launched into an "hysterical story" about how she drove to her senior prom on a fire engine. "It had us laughing so hard that most of us had to use the restroom afterward because we couldn't hold it in!" John recalls. "It just broke the ice." The opportunity to show her sense of humor relaxed the contestant and revealed a lighter, charming side of her personality that otherwise would have gone unnoticed. "Your sense of humor is so important," Moskal stresses. "That's one quality I really search for."

Due to its ability to energize an interview and improve a contestant's image, humor is a great interview tactic. "Laugh, make the judges laugh, have a good time," advises Cheryl Prewitt Salem. "Usually the girl who can laugh is the most relaxed because she knows who she is and is comfortable in herself."

Opening an interview with a touch of humor is an unrivaled ice-breaker. In 1988, Miss Ohio, Sarah Evans, kidded the judges about her unenviable position as the last of fifty interviews. "When I walked in there, they were all just sitting there," she recalls, mimicking their bone-tired expressions. "I said, 'Hi, I bet you're glad to see *me*!' I got a lot of laughs and it was a fun time."

Likewise, Catherine Lemkau, Miss Iowa 1992, used wit to begin her interview on a strong note. As the last contestant interviewed one morning, she capitalized on the approaching lunch hour. "Are you as *hungry* as I am?" she quipped before she'd even hit the chair. Not surprisingly, she became first runner-up.

For the contestant seeking to add zest to her interview, a sense of humor is a valuable asset.

39 · Understand "High-Gain" Questions

Since a titleholder's reign involves press conferences, interviews, and speeches, her ability to think under pressure, analyze complex and often controversial subjects quickly, and discuss them intelligently is critical. Judges use "high-gain" questions to determine if a contestant has those abilities. Since high-gain questions cannot be anticipated or "prepped" for, a girl can't regurgitate memorized answers. Thus, they reveal her *true* views and values, analytical skills, and mental alertness.

Often, that's the only way to pry behind the façades of contestants who give prerehearsed answers to hide the fact that they can't think under pressure. "So many contestants are prepared or programmed by their state pageants with memorized answers and opinions for any and everything," observes Sam Haskell, a veteran national judge and senior vice-president with the William Morris Agency. "Often when I'm interviewing I try to ask questions that the contestant will *not* be prepared for. That's the only way I can find out who she *is*."

Rex Holt, of GuyRex's Miss United States, explains that today's judges try to ask questions that require a contestant to share, not merely facts about a subject, but what she *feels* about the issue and how she would respond *to* the issue if personally involved. "We'll build a situation and ask you an either/or and a why so that you can express yourself," says Rex. "We encourage you to be opinionated—but be knowledgeable enough to back up your beliefs." He offers a sample question about conflict in Korea. "It's not about how much you know about politics in Korea at the moment, but about how you'd feel about your boyfriend or husband being called into service to go fight in Korea. It's to find out how well you express yourself, how well you carry on a conversation, how well you express your thoughts. Your verbal expression is shown through that type of question."

Contestants are encouraged to express themselves honestly. For instance, pageant guidelines often ask judges to look for an "independent, eloquent communicator with the 'courage of her convictions.'" Judges are told *not* to consider whether they agree with the girl's opinion, only whether she backs it up with sound reasoning. "Judges recognize differences of opinion," says state and national judge Dennison Keller. "If you back up your opinion, even though it is totally different from what the judge might believe, if there is logic behind it, no judge should ever count that against you. But many times you can come off too terribly aggressive," he adds, "so you've got to couch what you're saying in a conversational mode." In other words, speak your mind—but with warmth and sincerity.

Although high-gain questions cannot be fully anticipated, always try to answer questions calling for you to reason, analyze, or share your opinion.

40 · Never Place Yourself in an Unflattering Light

Memorize this: "She who guards her mouth and her tongue keeps herself from calamity." (Proverbs 21:23, paraphrased)

Remember that high-gain questions are revealing . . . and point-losers if mishandled. Judges don't expect contestants to be perfect, but they do expect them to show good judgment and speak with intelligence. During the titleholder's year, any slip of the tongue can end up in headlines, so a contestant's diplomacy and tact are critical to her duties if chosen as the winner. Therefore, before answering, consider the impression a statement will leave in judges' minds.

For instance, I once asked a student, "Who is your role model?" "Goldie Hawn is my number-one role model," she replied, adding, *"but I don't know much about her."* The young woman's answer made her sound insipid and unqualified to handle the public speeches and media interviews required of a titleholder. Consider how your answer will make you sound.

A high-gain question involving your personal views about a controversial subject must be handled tactfully. Consider the response of a national contestant who was asked, "What is the difference between discipline and child abuse?" Without thinking, the young woman launched into a vivid explanation to the effect: "Discipline is when a parent takes a kid out back to the shed and uses a switch or smacks 'em around on the leg with a stick. Child abuse is when there's blood all over the place and broken bones and stuff." We judges were so shocked we nearly fell off our chairs. If only someone had explained to the poor girl that there are many ways of stating the same point. Her opinion could have been expressed in better taste. Use tact.

Judges want the titleholder they select to possess the qualities of a winner. While they are charmed by sincerity and candor, judges are turned off by a girl who is so candid that she shocks the judges. Never express your views in a way that will place you in an unflattering light. Use good judgment when expressing yourself.

Many judges ask contestants to describe their most embarrassing experience. The answer reveals whether the young woman's sense of humor is wholesome or bawdy, and what she considers to be proper topics of conversation (what might she say in public during her reign?).

In response to this question, one local entrant launched into a story about a series of risqué mishaps she had endured on her way to a bar. In conclusion she exclaimed, "I looked like a *hooker* or something!" In one moment she blemished the lovely image she had created. Avoid mentioning words or subjects that have negative connotations: hooker, going to bars, bad grades, your first speeding ticket, or the time you got suspended from school. Obvious—but you'd be surprised how many contestants detonate otherwise fine interviews with such bombshells.

Remember, the only thing judges know about you is what *you choose to show them*. Every remark you utter creates a picture in judges' minds. *You* decide what picture you paint. Have you portrayed yourself as a Rembrandt—or something from the comic page? Don't place yourself in an unflattering light that might cause judges to question your suitability to represent your community as a titleholder.

41 · Make Your Faults Flattering

Judges also like to ask contestants to share a personal negative quality, typically her worst fault or feature, greatest failure, etcetera. Avoid answering such personal questions in a way that focuses attention on a *negative*: "My worst fault is that I talk too much and sometimes I say things that get me in trouble." Ooops. Hardly a quality judges want their winner to possess. If it doesn't make you look good, don't say it.

The safest strategy is to frame your answer *positively*: "I guess my biggest fault is being a bit of a workaholic. When I want to accomplish something, I'm very determined and dedicated so I have to work at taking time to relax."

Phrased positively, even a "worst fault" can become an admirable quality. Debra Wolfe, Mrs. America 1984, achieved the right balance in her response to the question, "What do you consider to be your best quality and your worst characteristic?": "My best quality probably would be my dedication to my priorities, just having my priorities in order and knowing what my roles are. My worst qualities probably would be occasionally doubting my own self-worth. . . . "[2]

Your goal is always to create a positive impression. Knowing how to make your faults sound flattering can take you a step closer to the crown.

42 · Don't Panic If You Don't Know the Answer

It's every contestant's nightmare. A judge asks you a question . . . the panel stares in your direction awaiting your answer . . . and your mind goes blank. You can't answer the question.

Don't panic! "Many girls make the mistake of hemming and hawing," notes Jeff Bell, a veteran pageant director. "They panic and start perspiring and look like they want to cry." Admitting you don't know an answer, Bell says, "just gives judges a chance to ask you about something you *do* know."

This usually applies to questions requiring a fact as the answer:

- Who is Sally Ride?
- What was the War Between the States?
- What is the First Amendment?
- Name the vice-president.
- Where is the Gaza Strip?

Failing to answer a fact question isn't fatal. In fact, Jennifer Sauder survived such a moment while competing for the 1987 Miss Florida title. Judges grilled her with a rapid-fire series of fact questions. When one stumped her, she admitted, "I'm sorry, I don't know that." Stumped by the next question as well, Jenny used the moment to prove she could handle tough spots with humor. "Sorry," she quipped, laughing, "I don't know *that* either." She became Miss Florida and made the national semi-finals. Likewise, Miss Americas Dorothy Benham (1977) and Elizabeth Ward (1982) each missed a question during their state pageants, won anyway, and went on to win the big one.

Even at the national level, missing a question need not damage a contestant's chances. During her national interview, Miss Michigan, Kaye Lani Rae Rafko, was unable to answer a judge's question. "If I didn't know something, I was honest," she admits. "There was one question where I didn't know the person so I said, 'I've never heard of that person before.' I was honest." Judges selected her as Miss America.

The *way* a contestant handles not having an answer makes all the difference. "If she tries to fake an answer, I'll know it," observes Sam Haskell. "If she honestly admits she's not prepared, or if she asks me to help her better understand the question, I'll point her." If you can't answer a question, ask the judge to rephrase the question, or calmly admit that you don't know, smile, and move on to the next question. Not knowing an answer is not a big deal . . . if you don't *make* it one.

43 · *Know What Questions You Must Answer*

While it is acceptable to occasionally admit you don't have an answer, never reply, "Sorry, I don't know," to a question that calls for your *opinion*. There are some questions you must answer or risk "flunking" your interview.

I recall judging a political science/international relations major who wouldn't answer any question that required her to think or stretch. When asked, "Do you think sales of nuclear arms to China should be banned?" she refused to even *attempt* to offer an opinion. Her cop-out, "Sorry, I'm not schooled on that," unquestionably lowered her scores and eliminated her from consideration. Frankly, we didn't expect her to be an expert on China. We simply wanted to see if she could think.

When a judge asks for an opinion about an unfamiliar subject, rather than losing points for not answering, Sam Haskell advises contestants to share their general thoughts on the subject. "I would rather a girl just say, 'You know, I don't really *know* about this, but I think if they'd do this . . .' or, 'You know, I've thought about that too, and while I don't understand it well enough to *know*, this is what I think. . . .' Whether she's 'right' or 'wrong,' I prefer realness." You won't always have a firm opinion about an issue the panel brings up. Rather than "passing" on a tough question, share whatever thoughts come to mind at that moment in a casual, conversational style:

- Admit that, while it's an interesting question, you haven't given it much thought before.
- Find the main point of the question.
- Mull it over quickly.
- Listen to your gut reaction.

- Share your thoughts with the judges ("It seems to me that . . .").

While judges realize that a contestant can't possibly have answers to every question, they do expect her to be able to think. If you don't have a definite opinion to offer, converse with the judges about the subject in a natural, friendly way. But always *try* to answer a question that calls for you to express an opinion.

44 · Be Flattered By a Tough Interview

Tough interviews are a compliment. The tougher the interview, the greater the compliment. Judges are thrilled to meet contestants who are so knowledgeable and confident that they can take the panel's most difficult questions and respond with intelligence and perception. Some judges deliberately disagree with an obviously promising contestant to see how she reacts under pressure. Does she confidently but graciously defend her convictions? Or does she "wilt" under a judge's apparent displeasure and change her views to appease him or her? Since most national winners encounter hostile reporters or protestors during their reigns, pushing a contestant's "hot button" during the interview reveals how she would handle difficult situations as the winner.

For instance, few contesants understand that judges probe to discover which women will back down if challenged on their convictions. When Miss Florida, Leanza Cornett, expressed her views on her platform, AIDS prevention, a member of the panel cross-examined her. Unfazed by an unsmiling celebrity challenging her, Leanza calmly reiterated her views—and gained points.

What Leanza couldn't have known was that the panel reserved the tactic for women whose performance suggested they could be contenders for the crown. The tough treatment was a vote of confidence and Leanza made points by sticking to her guns. I jotted these remarks in my notes: "Relaxed, courageous in her views, expresses herself strongly with no hesitation." Days later when Leanza appeared on *Larry King Live* as the new Miss America, she handled callers with the same unflappable composure we judges had "tested" during her pageant interview.

Never be unnerved by a panel that pushes, probes, and provokes. Pat yourself on the back. The judges think you're good enough to handle anything they can throw at you.

FIVE

The Winning Swimsuit

*Pageant contestants need to be at their absolute best
to be successful in swimsuit and win.*
MIKE FIFRICK, FITNESS COACH, MISS WORLD JUDGE

The swimsuit competition is the oldest event in pageantry, with Margaret Gorman crowned the "Most Beautiful Bathing Beauty in America" in 1921. The tradition has changed a lot since that era when contestants paraded down the beach in swim-dresses, bloomers, and knee socks. Today's swimsuit competitions reflect the fitness mania and figure-flattering fashions of the '90s.

The event differs from pageant to pageant in judging, swimsuit styles, and image. In pageants that emphasize beauty, like Miss USA, Miss Teen USA, Miss World, GuyRex's Miss United States, and Mrs. America, swimsuit is a major category usually worth one-third of judging. Contestants often wear identical swimwear or bikinis provided by a sponsor, and the modeling style is casual.

In the more conservative scholarship/talent pageants, swimsuit is the least-important phase. Miss America's swimwear segment counts for a mere 15 percent of scoring (talent and interview are worth *twice* that), contestants wear modest one-piece suits, and the modeling style is conservative.

The most recent trend in this competition is an increasing emphasis on fitness and athletics. The Miss America program has renamed the phase "Physical Fitness in Swimsuit" and now includes "statement of physical fitness" as a judging criterion. In some cases the swimsuit competition has evolved into an actual physical fitness event. In the Mrs. U.S. International and GuyRex's teen pageants contestants model in aerobic wear and sneakers, rather than swimwear, while America's Junior Miss entrants perform an onstage aerobic fitness routine worth 15 percent of scoring. "The athletic look is *in*," affirms pageant fitness specialist Sharon Turrentine, "and I don't think it's going to change."

What Judges Look For

While swimsuit competitions differ significantly, judges usually consider some of the following qualities:

- first impressions
- beauty of face and figure
- well-proportioned body
- good muscle tone
- proper level of body fat
- statement of physical fitness and health
- poise, posture, and carriage
- graceful walk and modeling
- confidence
- proper fit of the swimsuit
- overall presentation
- energy and charisma

SECRETS TO IMPROVE YOUR SHAPE

Regardless of the individual format and judging emphasis of a given pageant's swimsuit competition, there is no question about what it takes to win. Judging instructions may use vague terms like "pleasing proportions"—but judges award their highest scores to women who are in top physical condition: "the . . . contestant who gives you that quick positive picture when you see her coming toward you," observes Jeanne Swanner Robertson, a renowned humorist and national pageant judge. "You don't have time to say, 'Triceps look good, biceps are doing okay.' But the overall quick picture is the one that says, 'This is a physically fit young woman.'" In the swimsuit competition, a beautiful, healthy body in prime physical condition is a sure winner.

45 · Build a Winning Body

While most swimsuit experts agree that today's judges prefer a physique that is in top physical condition, exactly what does that mean? "A fit, tight body of average muscle," answers Mike Fifrick, founder of Fitness from Fifrick and a 1991 Miss World Pageant judge, "not overmuscled, not bulky, not stocky, not undermuscled, not skinny, not waifish. I think that a good goal for a pageant contestant is a low-fat body with average muscle."

How can a contestant develop such a winning body? Exercise. And lots of it. Indeed, the majority of entrants' figures require an effective, consistent exercise program to reach their potential. "The underlying factor is predisposed genetics," explains Joseph Christiano, owner of Body Redesigning by Joseph Christiano, and a renowned personal trainer to contestants and celebrities. "In other words, it's whatever amount of clay you have to work with and how well you take care of the clay. There are a few girls who 'bloom from the womb,'" he quips, "but I haven't met many. Most of them were either a major or minor overhaul. Now and then I'd get one who needed a fine-tuning, but for the most part it was a major overhaul."

Since transforming a body can be a daunting undertaking, many contestants turn to physical fitness experts for help. Mike Fifrick, personal trainer to Miss World 1990 and the first runners-up at the 1992 and 1993 Miss USA pageants, shares an example of how proper training can improve a contestant's chances. "When Erin Nance won the [1993] Miss Georgia-USA title, she was a gorgeous girl but she wasn't at her best at that point. Since her body fat was above twenty percent, in the twenty-two percent range, through cardiovascular exercise we reduced her body fat to fourteen or fifteen percent before the nationals. She was somewhat undermuscled, so she also did an intense strength-training program every other day to add a little muscle to her body. I think we did forty-three workouts in

(BODY REDESIGNING BY JOSEPH CHRISTIANO)

Sandy Frick, Miss Florida 1989, and swimsuit winner, demonstrates "flies"—a bustline builder recommended by personal trainer Joe Christiano.

twelve weeks in preparation for the nationals." The grueling routine paid off, Fifrick reports. "Erin became the first runner-up to Miss USA and won the Catalina swimsuit award."

As Erin's transformation demonstrates, you can make impressive changes in a surprisingly short period of time if you approach training with the right mental attitude. "It depends on her personal motivation," asserts Sharon Turrentine, founder of Shape Up With Sharon and a top pageant fitness specialist. "It depends on the importance that she puts on the program, if she is motivated, how hard she is willing to work, and if she is willing to spend the time. With a young woman between eighteen and twenty-two who has never had children, who is willing to work, within six weeks she'll be looking in the mirror saying, 'Why didn't I do this years ago?'"

Some girls' figures are more challenging and require more time to correct flaws. Contestants with problem figures need to work within a *realistic* time-frame. "It depends on the condition they are in when they start," says Christiano. "You need to look at where you're at physically and line it up with the pageant. It's all in your peaking within the time-frame you have."

When there simply isn't as much time to prepare as a competitor would like, Cheryl Prewitt-Salem recommends an intense program to "jump-start" the contestant's progress. "For a pageant girl who may not have time, I recommend that she literally go into a two-hour weight-training program *every day*."

Whatever the specific training program, it should meet the needs of the girl physically and financially. "She doesn't have to be on a weight program at a gym," advises Cheryl, star of several exercise videos. "It depends on the person and the amount of money she has. Sometimes gyms and trainers can be very expensive. I recommend to girls on a tight budget—which is the majority of girls—that they get sound advice. Many times you can get that by going to see somebody one time. You can also get good advice out of books and exercise videos."

Possible exercise programs include working out at a private gym, college weight room, or YMCA. Girls can also get in shape at home using free weights, exercising to aerobic/body-toning videos, and training on a stationary bike, stair-stepper, or treadmill. Be creative, and remember, no two training programs are identical:

- Miss Universe 1980: weights, running, swimming, dance
- Miss America 1980: jogging, stationary biking, sit-ups
- Miss America 1983: Weight lifting, jogging with leg weights
- Miss America 1986: 45-minute jogs up Mt. Olympus
- Miss Teen-USA 1991: soccer, basketball, softball
- Miss USA 1991: aerobics, step machine, floor exercises

Whatever training program you choose to get yourself in shape, remember that developing a winning figure doesn't happen overnight and it doesn't happen without commitment and dedication. "You can't wait until the last minute to train," warns Christiano. "The *last* thing [you] want to do is the thing [you] need *most*. You have to challenge yourself to the very day of competition to look your very best."

46 · Correct Point-Losing Figure Flaws

There's no doubt about it—in the swimsuit competition the first things a judge will mark points off for are figure flaws: wide hips, flabby thighs and arms, "saddlebags," a droopy derriere, a protruding tummy, or scrawny calves.

To transform a point-losing figure into a winning one, a contestant must correct such flaws to create the evenly proportioned, well-toned physique preferred by judges. The goal is to change the body's muscles and body fat to create the ideal proportions for *your* height and bone structure. "We consider symmetry of form," says Rex Holt, of GuyRex's Miss United

States, "meaning that someone who is six feet tall can weigh a hundred fifty pounds and have perfect symmetrical form. It's based on the unique bone structure and weight proportions of each person."

Fortunately, body symmetry is only partially determined by Mother Nature. The rest is flabby muscle tone and fat accumulations "earned" through unhealthy exercise and eating habits. Improve the bad habits and you improve the bad body. "Each person can make improvements," encourages fitness expert Mike Fifrick, who holds a Master of Science degree in fitness management and exercise science. "Genetics play an extremely important role in the shape of any person's body, but no matter what the genetics, every woman can make improvements. A girl with average genetics who works hard can achieve a good body and compete favorably with a girl who has good genetics, but who doesn't prepare herself."

An intensive body-building program can build curves in the right places and diminish curves in the wrong areas. The fastest, most effective (nonsurgical) way to redistribute curves and improve swimsuit-sabotaging figure flaws is with a complete fitness regimen. "A physical fitness program has three important stages: proper nutrition, aerobic activity, and weight training," explains certified physical fitness specialist Sharon Turrentine, a former champion body-builder and powerlifter. "The purpose of utilizing all three phases is to "get your body in its peak physical condition for your particular genetic, muscular structure."

The first phase of a balanced fitness program, working out with weights, can dramatically improve a woman's figure. "Weight training will firm, tone, and shape the body to its personal best," explains Sharon, who hosts her own television fitness program, "Shape Up with Sharon." "A woman can change or enhance the shape of her body with weight training. With a properly designed weight training program she can put on more curves where she wants them and diminish curves where she doesn't want them by shaping the muscle underneath the skin."

Shape Your Hips, Thighs, Legs, and Buttocks

The most troublesome figure flaw contestants cite is the area between the waist and knees: flabby inner thighs, "saddlebags," chunky thighs, big buttocks, and heavy hips.

The good news is that although this problem area is resistant, exercise and a low-fat diet can make a significant difference. Body redesigner Joseph Christiano recalls one client who overcame problem hips and thighs, went from 34-26-42 to 36-23-36, and walked off with the Miss Florida title. "She was pear-shaped with a very nice upper body and small waistline—but from the hips down it looked like a different body. We went to work and she lost something like four and a half inches off each thigh and over five inches off her hips. When the pageant committee saw her they couldn't believe the change."

There are generally two underlying causes for a point-losing lower body: Either excess fat is covering what otherwise could be a nice figure, or poor genetics and a sedentary lifestyle have resulted in flabby, poorly shaped muscles. In either case, improvements *can* be made. "It depends on the body and the body-fat percent," says Mike Fifrick, author of *Better Bodies for Beauties*. "If the bad hips and thighs are the result of too much body fat and she is dissatisfied with her shape, she needs to reduce her body fat first to see what her body looks like tight and firm. Slow, comfortable cardiovascular exercise will help, but it's got to be a lot of hours in a week to make an improvement. If the bad hips and thighs are the result of genetically shaped muscle, then it's a more difficult problem," he explains. "Then strength training may be the answer to changing the shape of those badly shaped hips and thigh muscles."

(SHARON TURRENTINE, INC., "SHAPE UP WITH SHARON")
Certified physical fitness specialist Sharon Turrentine
recommends lunges and squats for a winning lower
body.

Weight training is critical to reshaping the lower body. "The squat is the ultimate 'hip-eraser,'" says Turrentine, "if a woman uses the right form. The *way* a woman lifts weights is what's going to shape her body. It's not how much weight she lifts, but how she lifts the weights," she explains. "Women don't use a wide-foot stance because we're not going for power. If you are going for narrow hips and thighs and a 'runway body,' you need the proper form. Place the weight bar on the back of the shoul-

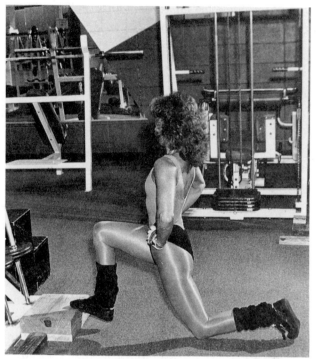

(SHARON TURRENTINE, INC., "SHAPE UP WITH SHARON")
"The squat is the ultimate 'hip eraser'," says Sharon.

ders, place the heels about four inches apart with toes pointed slightly outward for balance, squat until the thighs are parallel to the floor, and push back up with your heels. That makes the thighs rock-hard," says Sharon, "and it makes everything from the waist down narrow."

Another exercise guaranteed to improve the shape of the thighs is the "lunge." "We do our muscle *building* with the squats and our muscle *toning* with lunges with no weights," says Sharon, who trained several national swimsuit winners. "I have my women doing hundreds of lunges every day. They love 'em because they work. The more you do, the better your legs look."

Other exercises to tone, trim, and shape the lower body

include leg extensions, leg curls, seated leg presses, inner-outer thigh kicks, pelvic lifts, back and side leg lifts, and ballet pliés.

Shape the Lower Legs

An ideal swimsuit physique features well-shaped lower legs. Calf raises performed with three different positions (straight on, toes in, toes out) can shape, tone, or build up lower legs. Other calf shaping exercises include the seated calf machine and toe presses on a leg-press machine.

Slenderizing heavy lower legs usually requires aerobic exercise and a low-fat diet to trim excess fat, combined with multiple sets of high-repetition calf raises to shape the calf muscles.

Building up underdeveloped calves requires intensive training with heavier weights. "It's difficult," warns Fifrick, "so strength-train them with intensity. If you have skinny calves, you need to build some muscle, and the way to build muscle is to do the calf raises with as much resistance as [you] can handle, with great intensity." Such training can be grueling, but shapely calves are such an asset onstage that they are worth every moment of effort.

Broaden Shoulders to Look Slimmer

Another secret to improving the body's proportions is building up the upper back and shoulders. "The biggest thing I have to convince them to do is to *broaden* their shoulders," says Turrentine. "It gives you a more balanced look if you put width on the upper part of the body. A wider upper back and wider upper body make the waist and hips *appear* narrower."

"The American woman tends to emphasize and spend a lot of time working on the bottom part of the body," agrees Cheryl Prewitt-Salem, author of *How to Get a Balanced Body*. "You need to build your upper body to balance your lower body and give

(SHARON TURRENTINE, INC., PHOTO BY KEN PURCELL)
Sharon demonstrates how shapely lower legs can be
developed with calf-raises.

you the overall balance you need. You don't want to look like
a weight-lifter. You just want to be toned and have some nice
'cuts' in your shoulders, abs, and pecs. I recommend doing
[exercises for] bicep, tricep, and shoulders with light weights,
three- to ten-pound hand weights."

(SHARON TURRENTINE, INC., PHOTO BY KEN PURCELL)
Broadening the upper back with chin-ups creates the
illusion of a smaller waist.

Exercises for the shoulders and arms include lateral arm
lifts, military press, pull-downs, tricep pull-overs, bicep curls.
Swimming laps and rowing are also great shoulder builders.

Build the Bustline

The bustline/chest area also helps balance the lower body.
"Boobs are nothing but body fat," says Sharon, "but you can
build up the pectoral muscles [beneath] with the right type of
exercise."

Bench presses are ideal but they have to be done correctly. "When guys bench-press they bring the bar down to the center of the chest and straight back up. They're going for *power*. We are going for cleavage so we bring the bar down to the center of the *upper* chest to develop the muscles in the upper center of the chest. That makes a 'line,' so when the light onstage catches it, it gives you the appearance of a larger chest." Bench presses, push-ups, and butterflies are ideal for enlarging the muscles beneath the bustline, "so whatever bust is there has a bigger shelf to sit on," she quips.

An extra workout on the day of competition can help to pump up the chest area to its fullest, according to Joseph Christiano. "With Melissa [Aggeles], who won the swimsuit competition in 1988, we did an extra chest workout that day just to fill out her upper body. That's one of the tricks of the trade that I use to help a girl balance her figure for competition day."

Trim the Tummy

While a tiny waist has always been the ideal, a trim, toned and tan tummy is even more important in contests like Miss USA, Miss Teen USA, GuyRex's Miss United States, and Miss Hawaiian Tropic that allow or require two-piece swimwear for competition. "They have to spend more time working their abdominal area than girls in the Miss America system do," advises Sharon, "because it's going to show." Exercises to tone the area include sit-ups (some Miss USA finalists admit to doing a thousand a day), assorted abdominal "crunches," and leg scissors and leg lifts for the lower abdominals.

While exercising can tone the underlying muscle, most waist problems also involve excess weight around the middle. "Sit-ups do not reduce fat," says Mike Fifrick. "To have a tight stomach you've got to have very low body fat. Reducing fat as a result of cardiovascular exercise helps make your midsection smaller."

Achieving a flattering waistline depends upon both muscle-toning exercise *and* fat reduction. "There's an old saying in the world of body-building," says Joseph Christiano, chuckling, "'You can't flex *fat*.' You can exercise hard, but if you haven't gotten rid of the extra layer of fat which is between the muscle and skin, no matter how hard you crunch your abs, you can't see them." To whittle the waistline, combine muscle-toning stomach exercise with fat-reducing aerobic exercise.

Let Your New Curves Show

After a young woman has invested months of grueling exercise to obtain the body of her dreams, she won't want layers of body fat to hide her efforts. "One big factor in how a woman's body looks," says Fifrick, "is what her body-fat percent is—with a lower body-fat percent being better. It's not until you get your body fat less than twenty percent that you can actually see the shape of the muscles. If a woman is approximately twenty percent or higher in body fat, she has no definition. In other words, you can't see the shape of her muscles."

That's where aerobics enters the picture. "Aerobic activity is very important in a physical fitness program because it teaches the body to increase its metabolism, thereby burning excess calories more efficiently," Sharon Turrentine explains. All of which helps to reveal what all those hours of training have created. "As you burn excess body fat and improve the muscle tone between the waist and knees—the part of our bodies that we hate—your hips get narrower and firmer and you just *look* better."

"If you need to drop weight, aerobics is wonderful," agrees Cheryl Prewitt Salem, star of several aerobic workout videos. "Do whatever kind you like—step aerobics, plain aerobics, low-impact, high-impact—whatever works for you and that you enjoy." Aerobic exercise can also include stationary biking, cycling, jogging, long-distance running, fast walking, treadmill, stair-stepping, and swimming laps.

Overcome Excessive Thinness

Like any other figure problem, excessive thinness can hurt a contestant's chances. An extremely thin girl needs a training program to *build* muscle (curves). Fortunately, starting off on the skinny side can be a blessing in disguise, simply because every ounce of muscle she gains through training immediately *shows*. "Jennifer Prodgers, Miss Georgia-USA 1992, is the best example of that," says Mike Fifrick. "She was extremely low in body fat and undermuscled to begin with. Not that she was 'skinny,' but she was definitely slender. She strength-trained consistently and with intensity and improved a body that some thought was *too* thin. With a good strength-training program, she changed from being close to skinny to being someone who is very shapely. She has an outstanding swimsuit body and she was top six at Miss USA and second in the final swimsuits."

Excessive thinness needn't hold any young woman back from competing successfully, asserts Fifrick. "A thin girl needs to strength-train with intensity because that's a way of adding some muscle to her body to make her look less skinny."

47 · Eat to Win

Exercise is only the first step in preparing a figure for the swimsuit competition. The second step is eating to win. "Weight training is what *shapes* the body," explains Sharon Turrentine, "but if she does not eat right and does not do aerobic activity, the shape remains covered with a layer of excess fluid and body fat and she won't see the changes. Her physical fitness level will be improving on the inside but she won't be able to see it. Therefore she thinks nothing is happening, she becomes discouraged, and she quits. Eating right is the bottom line."

Debra Maffett, Miss America 1983, is a great example of how proper nutrition can help transform a figure. "I worked my way through college working at a bakery," she recalls. "I didn't know anything about good nutrition and I was very, very unhealthy. I was really into junk food and I had a weight problem." After her boyfriend jokingly called her "thunder thighs" Debra began an exercise program and changed her eating habits. "I started eating fresh vegetables, fruit, and lean meats. To think that years later I won the swimsuit competition in Atlantic City—when at one time I was twenty pounds overweight!"

Eating to win isn't complicated. "Here is the secret to good nutrition," says Turrentine. "Your third-grade teacher taught you this: three balanced meals a day, foods from the four basic food groups, and the proper portions on your plate—period." Of course, that can be a tough prescription for a generation of teenage girls brought up on junk food. "It is difficult to do because our society doesn't accept proper nutrition. Fast foods are a lifestyle for most people." Still, Turrentine insists that junk food has no part in a serious contestant's diet. "Any 'food'— and I use that term loosely—that one consumes from a paper bag from a drive-in window should not be consumed by a human being!" She chuckles. "And especially not someone who is going to put on a swimsuit and walk out on a stage in front of millions of people."

What is a winning diet comprised of? "About fifteen percent of your total caloric consumption should be protein," advises Mike Fifrick. "The emphasis in the diet should be on complex carbohydrates: pastas, potatoes, rice, wheat breads, grain cereals and, of course, fresh fruits and vegetables are great."

High-fat foods have no place in a winning diet. "It's simple," says Turrentine. "Fatty foods make you fat. There's no mystery to it." Indeed, fat is the first item yanked off a state winner's menu. "I would recommend that a pageant contestant, like anyone else, eat a low-fat diet," says Fifrick. "That isn't to deny themselves food. It's to make better food selections. There are plenty of low-fat foods that are tasty. I encourage them to find those foods that they like to eat that aren't so high in fat."

Tips

- Fat calories are converted to body fat much easier than calories from other foods. You eat fat . . . you get fat.
- Researchers report that "starvation diets" change the metabolism by putting the body into "survival mode"—making it harder to lose weight.
- Water suppresses hunger and helps flush fat and waste out of the body. Aim for at least eight glasses a day.

48 · Control Your Body Chemistry at the Pageant

Maintaining a healthy body chemistry during competition is critical to success in the swimsuit competition. Any change in body chemistry can harm a contestant's chances by hurting her appearance onstage. Water retention and weight gain due to PMS or menstruation is a common problem. "A girl can look great, but that particular week or getting into that week, she'd be five pounds heavier," explains Joseph Christiano. "Her hormones are upside down, her water retention is up, and all of her work is going to go down the tubes if we don't adjust for that."

You can't make the menstrual cycle cooperate for competition, but careful planning can help prevent any accompanying water retention. To combat bloating, says Joseph, some contestants take "a vitamin-B complex with an additional vitamin B_6 which works as a natural diuretic." Further, he says, "I make my girls drink lots of water to pass water. You don't retain water if you drink lots of water, because you're hydrated." But if a young lady does not consume enough water, "The body signal is, 'We're dehydrating so let's retain water.' Then she balloons up!" Remember to drink plenty of water.

Sudden changes in eating habits during pageant week are another common problem, causing unflattering water retention that makes a young woman look puffy in her swimsuit. "The problem is that when they leave their state and go to [the nationals] the chow wagon is just garbage," explains Christiano. "The sodium content is much higher than the pretty strict diet the girls are on when they're preparing. Consequently, they're overloading on salts."

Since the resulting water retention can bloat an otherwise trim contestant, Christiano invariably spends pageant week biting his nails. "I'd be a 'nervous father' all week hoping they'd hang in there and not go 'blow-up'!" He recalls one national contestant who had a terrific figure and had won her state swimsuit competition. After training the young woman for a year to get her into superb condition, Joseph sent her off to the nationals, confident she was a top contender. When he saw her two weeks later, he was shocked speechless. "I couldn't believe it! She just blew up overnight. It looked as if she had swallowed an air hose!" Between her period and a suddenly high-salt diet, her body ballooned with water weight. "It looked like she put on fifteen pounds. Well, you don't get fat in one week, but the sodium content was so much higher." He sighs. "There was a girl who had worked hard to get her body in shape. She was going to be a real threat, very competitive, but when she walked on that runway it was over." Her body cycles and a suddenly unhealthy diet conspired to sabotage her chances.

"Peaking [being at 100 percent top form *that day*] is the most important part," says Christiano. "After all the work is done, if you don't peak on that day you're not going to look your best, and of course, you're not going to score as well. You need to peak at the right time."

When a young woman has worked for years to achieve her

dream, it's devastating to watch a temporary water gain ruin those efforts. Proper diet is the key to preventing, or at least diminishing, such problems. "You've got to eat right," asserts Sharon Turrentine. "Fluid retention comes from excess sodium in the diet. Of course, physical problems can also cause that, but as a rule, excess sodium is what causes fluid retention. If she is eating right, that is going to be such a small factor it won't make a difference."

During competition week most pageants provide an assortment of foods and beverages backstage and room service at the hotels. Contestants can maintain a healthy low-salt, low-fat diet by making careful food choices. Some girls stock their hotel room with fruit, bottled water, and pop-open cans of water-packed tuna for healthy, on-the-go snacks. When eating backstage between rehearsals or at pageant-week luncheons, dinners, and parties, choose fruits, vegetables, and lean meats. Avoid pastries, fried chicken, hamburgers, pizzas, deli sandwiches, and hors d'oeuvres which are loaded with fat and salt that contribute to water retention and bloating.

Carefully control your eating habits during competition to keep your body in healthy condition. Don't allow a change in diet or unruly body chemistry to derail your dreams.

THE PERFECT SWIMSUIT

So you've changed your eating and exercise habits to build your perfect body. Now it's time to find the right swimwear to put on it. The ideal swimsuit should make your figure look well proportioned, camouflage figure flaws, create a winning image, and help you stand out from the crowd. Since your choice of suit can dramatically alter how you look onstage, you don't want to settle for just a pretty swimsuit. You want the *perfect* swimsuit.

49 · "Regular" Swimsuits Need Not Apply

When your swimsuit can mean the difference between success and failure, you don't want to take chances. Luckily, you won't have to. Today's pageant swimsuits are marvels of modern engineering designed especially for stage competition. "A swimsuit for the stage is not even close to a suit you would swim in," says Cheryl Prewitt Salem, founder of C.P. Annie Productions, Inc., a leading pageant swimwear manufacturer. "They have to be specially constructed for the stage." Today's swimsuits sport high-tech fabrics, linings, and camouflaging designs to fool the eye and flatter the figure. "There is an art, a technique to this," admits pageant clothier, Thomas Tolbert, of Georgia's Legends. "It's no longer just grab something and go on with the pageant."

No doubt about it, the swimsuit competition has gone high-tech. Many pageant apparel shops even feature state-of-the-art "lighting rooms" equipped with runways, stage lighting systems, and video equipment aimed from the judges' eye level to record how a customer looks in various styles and colors. "We have the girls try on all the styles and all the colors to see which suit makes her look her very best," says Nancy Fish, co-owner of Arkansas' K.T.'s The Winning Edge. "Then we have her walk in the suits in different lights. . . . You've got to do whatever you can to be on top of the game and beat the competition."

Often the choice of swimsuit will depend upon the pageant a young woman is entering. Styles fall into three categories. In scholarship pageants, like Miss America, contestants wear conservative, lined, constructed, one-piece swimsuits in a solid color with a leg cut-up no higher than the front hipbone. In traditional beauty pageants like Miss USA, Miss Teen USA, and GuyRex's Miss United States, swimsuits are less conservative, often two-piece suits, with a higher-cut leg and derriere. In bikini contests, like Miss Hawaiian Tropic, entrants compete in barely there string bikinis.

Selection of an appropriate style is much easier now that many major pageant systems have sponsoring swimwear companies that provide or sell regulation swimwear to contestants. As of 1994, the Miss America, Miss USA, Miss Teen USA, GuyRex's Miss United States, Miss Teen All American, and Mrs. America pageants each used an official swimwear line.

But what if the pageant you are entering doesn't have a swimwear sponsor? Will any swimsuit do? Rarely. Regular department store swimsuits are seldom suitable for stage competition because they are insufficiently lined for modesty under intense stage lights and lack the construction and styles needed to properly shape the body onstage. Contestants who are serious about scoring highly should wear swimwear designed specifically for stage competition. Pageant swimwear is available in pageant specialty shops and some bridal boutiques, or by mail order. Swimwear can be ordered from some pageant swimwear collections with custom features such as higher-cut legs, shorter or longer "girth measurements" (to fit short or long torsos), and extra-large bra cups. Swimwear designers can also custom-make competition suits from scratch for hard-to-fit figures.

The two major factors in swimsuit competition are the body and what covers it. After you invest months of time and effort perfecting your physique, make sure what decorates it creates the best possible "frame" for your work.

50 · Flatter Your Figure With Perfect Fit

But even the finest swimsuit can flop if its *fit* doesn't do the body justice. "Fit is so important with your swimsuit," says Debbie Brown, of South Carolina's Brides & Beauties. A suit that fits poorly will emphasize figure faults and hurt the contestant's overall look. A perfectly fitted suit will create a sleek look that enhances even an average figure. "You can alter a swimsuit just like you can alter a dress," explains Debbie, who worked with 1993 America's National Teenager, Miss America 1994, and Miss USA 1994. "Alteration is everything."

The fit of a swimsuit also affects how a young woman *feels* onstage. "Fit is the most important thing," asserts Tricia Copelin, a swimwear designer and owner of Custom Creations by Tricia. "If the suit fits well she is going to feel well in it, and she is going to project confidence." Miss America 1990 is a case in point. Although Debbye Turner won the Miss Missouri title wearing a yellow suit, officials suggested she order a custom suit for the nationals. When the new swimsuit arrived days before the pageant, Debbye discovered it didn't fit as well. Despite speedy alterations, she still had reservations. "It wasn't exactly right—but I knew my yellow suit fit perfectly and I felt much more comfortable in it. My director told me, 'You do whatever makes you *feel* better.'" Turner decided to wear the original, better-fitting, yellow model and won the swimsuit competition—and the crown.

Swimsuit Fit Checklist

- Good fit is neither loose, nor so tight that the suit cuts into the shoulders, arms, legs, back, or bust.
- Fabric should mold against torso at all points with no wrinkles around bust, sides, abdomen, hips, or waist.
- No puckers should appear when the body is moving.
- Seat should smoothly cover and support the entire derriere. No wrinkles or exposure of derriere cheeks.
- Brassiere should not be so tight that the bust appears to be straining to pop out. (Remember to do fittings with any "padding" you plan to use.)

When you've worked for months to develop a winning figure, make sure you flatter your new-and-improved form with flawless fit.

51 · *Camouflage Figure Flaws With Style*

The right style is also important to a winning look. Thanks to high-tech pageant swimwear companies, contestants now have access to a host of styles designed to emphasize assets, camouflage figure flaws, and improve a contestant's figure onstage. But using such designs to full advantage requires knowing your figure. "Develop a personal analysis of your figure—your assets, what you need to hide, and what you need to bring out," advises Kathleen Munson, of Minnesota's The Pageant Shop.

Evaluating a girl's figure helps the contestant and her wardrobers determine the most flattering design. "You need to really look at what that particular body is like and adjust the swimsuit to what she looks like," advises Vernon DeSear, who supervised Miss Floridas' wardrobe selection for years. "There are many ways that you can take an average figure and make it look great because of the suit and the fit of the suit—regardless of the type of figure she has."

Improving a contestant's figure by creating flattering optical illusions makes such a difference onstage that body redesigner Joseph Christiano conducts a "swimsuit analysis" for his clients. "I have them model half-a-dozen swimsuits in different cuts and colors. I take front and back Polaroid shots of each, and we lay them out, study them, and make comparisons." Joseph will point out the optical illusions each style creates on the girl's body. "I'll show her, 'See how this cut compliments your lines? See how much better you look here, how it makes your legs look longer?' The minute you make comparisons with photos, it makes all the difference in the world—and they see it."

So do the judges—although their response is often a gut reaction. "Sometimes I don't think the judges *know* what they're looking for," says Christiano, "but the initial first impression, those first lines you see, are going to influence their scoring. If a girl comes out and her swimsuit cuts the lines of her body,

(C.P. ANNIE PRODUCTIONS, INC.)

"The right swimsuit can greatly improve how your figure looks onstage," says Cheryl Prewitt-Salem, of C. P. Annie Productions swimwear. Swimsuit styles, colors, and fabrics can help camouflage figure flaws and improve proportions.

then the judges could get a negative reading and give her less of a score—and not really know why. If the swimsuit's cut and color are wrong, you can lose points just on that. If girls are not aware of that, it could be to their detriment. Once your body is in shape, we have to get all the lines flowing so when you come out onstage, it all creates the right illusion for the judges."

Many figure flaws can be concealed, camouflaged, or balanced with clever swimsuit design and optical illusion. Here are guidelines from experts in pageant swimwear:

- Whatever your figure flaw—emphasize the opposite.
- The eye follows the line of your swimsuit.
- Vertical lines lengthen and slenderize.
- Horizontal lines shorten and broaden.
- Diagonal lines can slenderize and add curves to the waist, but can also cut torso length.
- Curved lines soften and add curves.

52 · Camouflage Figure Flaws With Fabric

Just as design can camouflage figure flaws, fabric finish can "improve" a figure. "The *shine* of the fabric can make a real difference," says Cheryl Prewitt Salem.

To slenderize a figure, cover it with a matte fabric. "If you put a dull fabric next to a shiny material, the shiny material is going to reflect light and look bigger," explains Thomas Tolbert. "If you wrap yourself in it, *you're* going to look larger. If you use a dull fabric, you still get the intensity of the color, but it will absorb light so you won't look nearly as big. It can take three to eight pounds off you, where the shiny fabric will *add* three to eight pounds."

To add the appearance of increased weight to a very thin body, cover it with a shiny fabric. "I only like the shiny swimsuits when the girl is very, very thin, because it adds weight," says Thomas. "If you are that thin and you don't want to look anorexic—that's when you need the shiny material."

Few contestants realize that pageant swimwear companies can make swimsuits from either side of the same fabric—using the glossy "right" side or the matte "wrong" side. Some companies now routinely cut their off-the-rack swimwear from the wrong side of the fabric to utilize the more popular dull finish. However, customers who special-order a swimsuit or have one custom made can usually specify whichever finish they prefer.

Whatever your figure type, the right fabric texture can improve the appearance of your figure onstage.

53 · Camouflage Figure Flaws With Color

Color is another effective tool for camouflaging a less-than-perfect figure. Use color to guide judges' eyes to make them see what you want them to see. "To get the best color," says Tolbert, "you've got to look at [the contestant] and ask, 'Does this color make me look at her face?' 'Does this color make me look at her legs?' 'What does this color make me *look at?'*

Color can draw judges' eyes to a negative or a positive. Few contestants realize that their swimsuit colors can unintentionally call attention to a problem area. For instance, dark colors, especially black, create a visual "collision" where the dark fabric meets a lighter thigh, drawing attention to the contrast spot, which is a common cite for point-losing figure problems. Avoid colors that create an obvious contrast near a figure flaw.

On the positive side, color can be an effective visual magnet to pull judges' eyes off a problem area and onto an attractive feature. Let's say that a contestant has a slender, well-shaped torso, but chunky legs. A swimsuit in an eye-catching bright, neon, or "hot" color would pull judges' attention onto the "magnet" color and the pretty torso it covers and off the problem legs.

Color can also be used to change the apparent shape of a figure. For instance, black defines the shape it covers. As such, a black swimsuit draws judges' eyes to the *outline* of a contestant's figure. If her body is unbalanced—perhaps an exaggerated pear shape—black would be the worst choice because it would "advertise" that flaw. A better choice would be swimwear in a medium shade like rose, peach, lavender, or pastel blue or green. Because medium colors are closer to skin tones, they create an uninterrupted monochromatic line that pulls judges' eyes over the figure in one fluid motion, thus deemphasizing any lack of balance. The right color can deemphasize figure flaws to create the visual illusion of a well-proportioned body.

Contestants can also use color to alter their apparent height and weight, making a tall, gaunt body appear shorter and curvier, or a short figure look taller and slimmer. Kylene Barker, Miss America 1979, who is very petite at five foot three, chose a yellow swimsuit to visually create a long, unbroken line from head to toe that made her *appear* taller. Conversely, Elizabeth Ward (1982), who is nearly five foot ten inches and ultra-thin, visually cut her height by "interrupting" her body with a dark cranberry red swimsuit and matching shoes.

Like these former winners, you can use clever color choices to improve your figure proportions. "Keep in mind that you want to look *balanced*," advises Evelyn Ay Sempier, a popular former Miss America and national judge. "As a judge looks at you from top to bottom, you don't want his or her eye to stop anywhere. You want it to move very quickly [over you] because there is a nice even look about you."

At A Glance

Balance the Body With Fabric Color
- White advances and makes the body look larger.
- Black/dark colors recede, making the body look smaller and denser.[1]

- Dark colors can interrupt the eye and cut body length.
- Black sharply defines the shape of the body.
- Eyes STOP where dark fabric meets lighter thighs.
- Primary colors draw attention.
- "Hot" and neon colors are the most attention-getting. Don't wear them on a problem area.
- Pastels "interrupt" body lines less.
- To appear taller and thinner, create one uninterrupted line with medium colors closer to skin tone.

As you shop for the perfect swimsuit for your figure, take along this handy guide to figure camouflage for style ideas. (Be sure to refer to Tips #51 to 53 as well.)

54 · Guide to Swimsuit Figure Camouflage

Find Your Figure

Wide Hips / Heavy Thighs:
- Broaden top of body to deemphasize wide hips.
- Wear widely spaced shoulder straps.
- Draw eye up with detailing of shoulders or bodice.
- Get leg opening cut higher at front center of thigh.
- No tight leg elastic or low, straight leg openings.
- Bust padding slightly out on sides for upper width.
- Avoid dark colors (they stop eyes at body's widest point— hips and thighs—thus widening more).
- Avoid white, bright, neon colors (they add weight).
- Create an even, slimming line with medium shades closer to skin tone and clear or skin-tone shoes.

Large Buttocks:
- Cover derriere fully! Avoid cheek exposure.
- Call attention off derriere; emphasize another area.
- Choose a swimsuit with a low-cut deep-**V**-shaped back.

- No high-cut backs, avoid round or square-shaped backs.
- Try bare-back styles or pretty straps on upper back.

Heavy Torso / Nice Legs:
- Get the attention off the torso.
- Avoid eye-catching colors that attract attention.
- Dark shades can help recede body and emphasize legs.
- Try a simple suit with no eye-catching detailing.
- Draw eyes down to legs with pretty shoes. Try a matching-color trim on clear acrylic shoes.

Slender Torso / Heavy Legs:
- Get the attention off the legs.
- Avoid dark colors, which cause legs to stand out first.
- Wear eye-catching colors to draw attention to torso.
- Tan the legs and wear "invisible" shoes.
- Wear detailing on upper swimsuit, pad bustline.

Straight Body:
- Any style that defines the waist will add curves.
- Diagonally crossed wrap bodices "create" curves.
- Supersuit pulls in waist.
- Halter brassiere with tight waistband adds curves.

Small-Busted:
- Bust padding adds fullness and "creates" a bustline.
- Taping breasts together creates cleavage (then pad). (See Tip #59, "Secrets of Anatomical Alterations.")
- Underwire bras and sewn-in bra cups add fullness.
- Try wrap bodices, gathering under or between breasts.

Large-Busted:
- Minimize bustline with good fit and extra support.
- The "supersuit" has the most bust support.
- Moderate **V** neckline (not plunging).
- Order a suit with custom extra-large bra cups.

Short Legs:
- Wear "invisible" shoes to make legs look longer.
- Get front center of leg opening cut in a high **V**.
- Create a taller unbroken line with a color closer to skin tone.

Narrow Shoulders:
- Thin, widely spaced shoulder straps widen shoulders.
- Avoid halters, turtleneck swimwear.
- Do you have long hair? Wear hair down to cover shoulders.

Too-Broad Shoulders:
- Thick shoulder straps close to neck draw eye inward.
- Try halter and turtleneck styles.

Long Torso:
- Use horizontal lines to "cut" a long torso.
- Try diagonal seams, wrap suits, or wide waistbands.
- Double-seam "supersuit" cuts torso length.
- Choose a high-cut leg to make torso look shorter.
- Order your usual swimsuit size in "long."

Short Torso:
- Lengthen torso with vertical lines or no lines.
- Don't break body length with horizontal lines.
- Try straight or princess lines, one-seam "supersuit."
- Wrap styles or double-seam supersuits cut torso length.
- Order a custom suit with a shorter "girth measurement."

Too Short:
- Dark colors and horizontal lines make body look shorter.
- Create a long, uninterrupted body line with medium shades closer to skin tone and "invisible" shoes.

Too Thin:
- Wear white, bright, or neon colors to add weight.
- Choose shiny fabrics to look heavier and curvier.

Average Body With Minor Figure Flaws:
- A monochromatic look with medium colors closer to skin tone creates a longer, slimmer, more balanced body line (but never wear a skin-tone nude color!).
- Best monochromatic looks are medium pink and peach.

Contestants with multiple figure flaws should "correct" their problems in order of importance, tackling the most obvious and potentially point-losing flaw, then the next, and so on.

While figure camouflage can conceal common figure flaws, there will always be those lucky—or hard-training—individuals who can afford to wear anything. "If they have a flawless body," says swimwear expert Tricia Copelin, "it's not going to matter what they have on. They'll look great in it."

55 · *Color Yourself Confident*

The right color can not only make you look like a winner, it can make you *feel* like one. "My theory," says Copelin, "is that [contestants] should always go with what they feel best in and what they look best in. I'm not of the theory that judges don't like certain colors. I think judges have enough sense to recognize what a girl looks good in and what a girl doesn't look good in. I mean, they're supposed to be judging the girl on her appearance *in* the suit—not on the color of the suit. Wear what you feel best in, because if you feel like you look dynamite, you're going to project confidence. And the judges are going to pick up on that."

Debbie Bryant-Berge a past swimsuit winner agrees that color can be a confidence booster. "I think anything that can make you feel a little bit better about yourself is important— even if it's just the color you are wearing." Realizing that she wanted a cheerful color that would boost her confidence onstage, Debbie chose bright yellow. "It was a good color because it made me feel happy and sunshiney. Anything that you can do to increase your self-confidence is all the better. It doesn't make any difference if it didn't make me look any better," she says, chuckling. "It made me feel better. And that's what is really important."

Color yourself confident.

56 · Understand "Color Psychology"

Color psychology can offer a competitive edge in two ways. First, color can help a candidate stand out from the crowd onstage. Second, color can craft the correct image for a pageant, thereby helping a contestant to impress judges as the potential titleholder.

Stand out in Group Judging

Color psychology can be used as a strategy to stand out from the crowd in group comparison judging, where contestants line up side-by-side in front of the judges.

For example, one famous pageant used group judging for decades. Judges had to quickly compare a lineup of ten to seventeen figures and give scores to only the five contestants who most impressed them. Obviously, anything that helped a girl catch the judges' attention could improve her chances of earning points. The most successful swimsuit colors were white and bright yellow, followed by bright pinks, and sky to aqua blues. Dark colors fared the worst. Why? Research affirms that white and bright colors are visual magnets. The *advance* visually while dark colors *recede* into the background. Further, the eye is attracted to colors in a specific order, starting with the bright, high-visibility colors, then to medium-bright shades, and last to dark recessive colors. Therefore, in group judging, catching the judges' eyes with white or bright colors is the winning strategy.

Of course, in contests that provide identical swimsuits, no such color advantage can exist. For instance, in the Miss USA, Teen USA, Universe, and Teen All American pageants, semi-finalists usually wear identical sponsor swimsuits. Likewise, semi-finalists in the Miss America Pageant now wear sponsor's swimwear in limited or identical color choices, depending on the year. Therefore, in these major systems, a contestant in a virginal white supersuit *can't* have an edge over some untutored gal in a bland brown number. The field is "level" so to speak.

While competitive edges through color psychology have been eliminated in the major systems, many other pageants continue to use comparative group judging and allow their entrants free choice in swimwear. A girl competing in such contests can increase the odds of judges noticing her and giving her high scores in the swimsuit competition by wearing eye-catching colors such as white, yellow, "hot" or neon colors, and medium-bright pastels. Catch their eyes with color psychology.

Convey the Right Image

Of course, merely catching judges' attention is not enough. The color must be both eye-catching and the correct image for that pageant.

For instance, over the past three decades, the swimsuit colors statistically most likely to win Miss America were high-visibility colors that also conveyed the feminine, nonaggressive "Cinderella" image befitting that title: white (virginal), yellow (happy), pink (feminine), and sky blue/aqua (soothing like the sky and sea). Of the past 36 winners, 13 wore white, 7 wore pinks, 6 wore yellow, and 5 wore shades of sky to aqua blue.

The top scorer, white, is an ideal color for competition because it is an attention-getting color that projects the ele-

gantly wholesome image winners are noted for. "White represents purity," says swimwear designer Ada Duckett. "It's a clean color."

Another highly successful color, yellow, has several advantages. It's eye-catching (the first color the brain registers), makes observers more alert, and is instantly associated with happiness and sunshine. That's a tough combination to beat. That's why, although yellow hasn't been a common swimwear color, when it has shown up, it has enjoyed a superb track record.

Medium pinks and blues fare well because they are soothing colors reminiscent of childhood and complimentary to many complexions and hair colors. Pinks flatter the body just as the right lipstick flatters the face, and have the advantage of being subconsciously associated with pleasant tastes and smells. Blues fare well because blue is the favorite color of two-thirds of Americans. Research has shown that sky blue actually has a soothing effect on people (judges). Aqua blue, another popular swimsuit color, was found to be one of men's favorite colors to see on females.[2,3]

Further, white, pink, yellow, and medium blue all are attention-getting enough to stand out onstage while also conveying the classically feminine image necessary to do well in wholesome pageants.

Bold *sexy* colors, like neon orange, are also visual magnets, but they can project too aggressive an image for scholarship pageants. However, they would fare very well in a pageant noted for its sexy image. For instance, at the 1978 Miss Venus-USA Pageant, Miss Michigan, DeDe Russell, used a neon-orange swimsuit to emphasize her curvaceous figure, long

Age is no barrier to fitness, says personal trainer, Joseph Christiano, whose client, Cindy Duhm, Mrs. Florida 1991, became a national swimsuit winner and first runner-up to Mrs. America.

(JOSEPH CHRISTIANO, "BODY REDESIGNING BY JOSEPH CHRISTIANO")

blond hair, deep Bahamas tan, and sultry walk. The resulting image conveyed to perfection a sexy "lifeguard centerfold" image. She brought the house down during the swimsuit competition and easily walked off with the Miss Venus-USA title. A "Cinderella color" wouldn't have come close to the impact of that little orange number. Hot orange was both eye-catching and sexy enough to project the exact image she needed to win *that* title.

To use color psychology effectively, a swimsuit color should be bright enough to stand out onstage, while also projecting the right image for the pageant. (See Tip #88 for more on color psychology.)

While color camouflage and color psychology can be helpful in picking the ideal swimsuit, a stand-out contestant will gain the votes of the judges regardless of what she wears. "If a girl looks good and feels good," Ada Duckett affirms, "she'll be the winner no matter what color she wears."

THE FINISHING TOUCHES

You've built the figure of your dreams and clothed it in high-tech competition swimwear designed to make the most of your assets. Now it's time to add the finishing touches that complement and complete the image you've created to win the swimsuit trophy.

57 · Walk in the Winning Shoes

The right shoes complement a contestant's body lines and slenderize and lengthen her legs. To create the most flattering head-to-toe "picture," experts recommend that contestants wear understated high heels, usually skin-tone leather full-pumps or clear acrylic sling-back shoes. "The trend is toward the beige or neutral-colored shoe and the clear plastic [shoe]," says Paula

Miles, director of six Miss USA/Miss Teen USA state pageants. "The beige and neutral are the best as far as I'm concerned. They make you look a lot sleeker, slimmer, and taller." The Miss USA, Miss Teen USA, and Miss Universe pageants usually supply contestants with identical skin-tone leather pumps for swimsuit competition. Likewise, most recent Miss Americas have worn clear or skin-tone pumps.

Dyed-to-match pumps and white shoes are *not* recommended because they draw too much attention to your feet. "You have to remember, the judges are usually on the floor and you're on the stage—and the one thing that is eye level to a judge is your *feet*," explains Cheryl Prewitt Salem, of C.P. Annie Productions footwear. "Never, never, never wear white shoes on the stage," she advises. "That's the first thing they're going to see. It's going to reflect light, it's gonna be big, it's gonna be bright—and it's not what you want."

The most recent trend in the swimsuit competition is away from footwear entirely. Richard Guy and Rex Holt, of GuyRex Associates, pioneered the barefoot competition format and have continued the no-shoes tradition in their GuyRex's Miss United States Pageant. "The girls feel so much better," observes Guy, "and if they feel good they'll look good." In 1994, the Miss America Pageant announced its decision to adopt a more casual swimsuit format with national contestants competing in bare feet during the event. Obviously, under such a policy, a young woman's feet are at judges' eye level, making a superb pedicure mandatory grooming.

58 · Look Slimmer With a Suntan

A suntan also contributes to a winning image in the swimsuit competition because it makes a young lady look slimmer, prettier, and more athletic.

Intense stage lighting washes out normal skin coloring, leaving most girls looking pasty and unhealthy. Therefore, contestants rely on a tan to help them appear more attractive onstage. "When I have a first-time contestant come in and she walks out under the special stage-lighting in our store, most often she'll go, 'Oh my gosh, I'm so white!'" remarks Robin Elliott-Bear. "They don't realize that their skin looks much lighter and washed out under stage lights. As much as I hate to say 'get a tan,' it does help them to look better and feel better about themselves onstage."

A suntan also makes a contestant look slimmer. Color principles that apply to fabrics also apply to figures. "Darker shades are going to make you look smaller," explains Tricia Copelin, "not only with clothing, but with your skin, too. You just look smaller when you are tanned."

Because tans are flattering and slenderizing they remain popular, but with the risk of skin cancer from both suntanning and indoor tanning beds, girls need to know that there is no "safe" tan.[4] Use caution and follow safety guidelines with any form of tanning. Many contestants achieve an attractive tan by combining self-tanning creams with a light natural suntan or moderate use of a tanning bed. "Basically, you want to be tan," says Copelin, "but you don't want to be so dark that you are doing damage to your skin."

Self-tanning products are ideal for hectic pageant schedules that prevent girls from suntanning outdoors. "They need a nice, healthy glow, but when you go to the state preliminaries, or Miss America, or Miss USA, they keep you so busy that you have no time to keep that golden tan," says Thomas Tolbert. "So what you do is get a good base tan and then use tanning creams to enhance it."

Because self-tanning products affect skins differently, always test them beforehand. "They can be very good," says Cheryl Prewitt Salem, "but you need to try them more than once before you get into competition. Some people's skin reacts to them. Some people's skin turns orange and other people get the most beautiful tan!" Since tanning products react differently, Tolbert advises contestants to "learn which one works best for you and how to apply it correctly."

59 · Know the Secrets of "Anatomical Alterations"

Today's pageant contestants are masters of "anatomical alteration" to achieve better proportions in swimsuit. Since most of these techniques focus on improving the bust, let me mention that contestants do *not* have to be busty to win. Dozens of small-busted women have won major titles including Miss World, Miss Universe, Miss USA, and Miss Teen USA, proving that the key to the crown is not a bigger bra size but a beautifully proportioned figure.

But for girls who choose to enhance their curves, padding and taping to create a larger bustline are permitted in most major systems, including Miss America and Miss USA. Always check the rules first.

Padding

A nice bustline is important because it balances a young woman's hips to achieve the evenly proportioned figure judges score highly. Unfortunately, statistics show that the average woman's bust is nearly two inches smaller than her hips. With "balanced proportions" being an actual judging criterion, and Mother Nature seldom manufacturing even hourglass figures, many young women feel they stand a better chance if they create those better proportions with padding. And, unlike breast implants, padding is a cheap, temporary, procedure that has no potential health affects.

Foam-rubber push-up pads without a fabric lining are a popular choice for use in swimsuits since they have no tell-tale seams. "And in a swimsuit fabric you will see a seam," says

Tricia Copelin. "It also makes them slippery on the outside" which can cause them to slide out of position. Some swimsuits have bra "pockets" to hold padding, but for regular suits, unlined foam-rubber pads stay in place well since they grip the skin.

Other contestants prefer to use silicone pads worn externally. These new high-tech falsies are popular because they look and move naturally. "It's a natural shape," explains Tolbert, "and because it's filled with silicone, once you 'tape,' you just place it over your breast and the body temperature makes them conform to the breast."

Taping

In addition to using padding to increase the bust, many contestants use taping techniques to create cleavage and shape the bustline. "It gives you a better figure," says Tolbert. "If you are small-busted or you have wide-set breasts, you can give yourself cleavage without having to have cosmetic surgery. A girl who is an A cup can tape and add silicone implants on the outside for fullness and look like a B or C cup." Taping can also be used for support. "With a lot of swimsuits and gowns you don't wear bras, so taping gives you support so you're not bouncing around onstage."

Not all tapes are alike. Some contestants prefer surgical adhesive tape available in drugstores, while others prefer easy-to-remove clear packaging tape. "I tell my girls to use UPS tape, the kind you tape boxes with," says Tricia Copelin, a pageant swimsuit designer. "It's less painful to get off than masking tape or surgical tape and it does just as good a job for the length of time they need to wear it. *Never* use duct tape or adhesive tape because it will take your skin off. That's dangerous!" (One contestant required hospital treatment to remove duct tape from her skin.) Always perform a "test tape" beforehand to check for allergic reactions and ease of removal.

Using proper technique is also important, says Copelin. "What has worked real well for me is to take a piece of tape about twelve to fourteen inches long. [While bending forward] without your bra on, stick the piece of tape to the outside of one breast. Pull your breasts together as close as you can with one hand, while you pull the tape straight across underneath the bottom of your breasts, and stick it on the other side. You stop right before you get to the armhole of your swimsuit. You're making a 'shelf' with tape in the middle that holds your breasts together. Then pad out a little on the sides."

Don't overdo the "anatomical alterations." I can't name names, but a top-level pageant official who trains national judges told me that obvious "engineering" can backfire. "Do it appropriately to create the illusion of a balanced figure," advised the anonymous official. "I've seen girls who created big busts—and I didn't consider that the illusion of a balanced figure because they had manipulated it. I consider that in my scoring, and I encourage my judges to do so too!" If you use padding and taping, don't cost yourself points by overdoing it.

Glueing

Another common practice is to apply an aerosol spray adhesive, popular with athletes, to the derriere to keep the swimsuit bottom in place onstage. "All the girls use Firm Grip to hold their swimsuit firm so it doesn't creep up while she walks the runway," says Tricia Copelin. "It's strictly for the girl to be sure that's she's covered up."

It's important to have the right technique. "You put the swimsuit on, pull it up away from your fanny, and spray the Firm Grip on your rear end," Tricia explains. "Then fan it with your hand for about thirty to forty seconds so it can get tacky. The trick to it is, when you spray it, don't immediately put the suit over it because it has to get tacky to work," she says. "Otherwise it will just soak into your suit. Don't pull the suit down over your fanny because it will smear it. Pull the suit away from your body, then place the suit down where it needs to be and smooth it."

"One of the hints I give my girls," says Copelin, "is to put a wet washcloth in a little Ziploc bag in their makeup kit a few hours before. After the swimsuit competition, wipe that stuff off their rear end so their dress doesn't stick to them." To get the knack of it, Tricia advises contestants to practice the technique with an old swimsuit.

60 · Pull It All Together for Points

Being successful in the swimsuit competition requires achieving a beautiful total picture: a great figure, flattering swimsuit and accessories, and good grooming.

Elegant carriage, walk, and posture add the winning touches to that overall picture. "Posture is one of the most important things to the total appearance," says Robin Elliott-Bear. "How you stand shows a lot about how you feel. It should be natural but graceful." Carriage and posture also affect how the swimsuit looks. "If she doesn't stand properly onstage her swimsuit is not going to fit properly. It throws everything off. If you don't stand with your shoulders back and your abdomen up and in, the swimsuit doesn't look good and your body doesn't look as good in it."

Confidence in a swimsuit is another point-getter because it reveals a young woman's ability to be self-assured in uncomfortable situations, a quality that is essential to a titleholder's reign. "The purpose of the swimsuit competition is to see if [contestants] can handle an uneasy situation," says Vernon DeSear, who has three decades of judging experience. "What I notice even more than the obvious 'face and figure' is how comfortable she appears. There should be a confidence there.

Let's face it, if you can stand in front of that many people in a swimsuit and maintain your confidence and ability to relate how you feel about yourself, I think you could do almost anything."

Because of the fast-paced atmosphere of judging, contestants must make an instant impression. Judges see a contestant in her swimsuit for only seconds before they must score her. In those moments each judge takes an instant mental "snapshot" of the girl's appearance from head to toe: body, swimsuit, hair, make-up, shoes, carriage, and confidence. The judge's instant reaction to that total image becomes the contestant's score.

When all is said and done, winning the swimsuit competition comes down to doing the best with what you've got and making sure it's perfectly packaged. As Joseph Christiano points out, some of the transformations are so impressive they surprise even him. "It's amazing that most of the young women were not in good shape when I met them," he says. "What you see is the *final product*. It's all window-dressed, wrapped, and painted, and looking gorgeous. I see them with their hair tied back, no makeup on, and in their old sweats. In fact, when I see them on the runway, I can't believe this is the girl I worked with. But it took months and months of hard work on their behalf to reach that level of fitness. People don't see what they go through, how hard they work and sacrifice to get there and look their best. I tell them, 'Win, lose, or tie—hold your head up high and smile, because you've gone the distance and put forth all that effort and sacrifice. The rest is up to the judges.'"

The Winning Talent

I don't think it matters what her talent is.
The girl is the one that wins it.
VERNON DeSEAR,
VETERAN NATIONAL JUDGE

The talent competition is one of the newer events in pageantry, added to the Miss America Pageant as an optional event in 1935 to show that entrants were more than pretty faces. In the half a century since, talent has been a popular part of the pageant industry.

While beauty pageants like Miss USA don't include a talent phase, most scholarship pageants traditionally do require talent. In fact, in the Miss America system, talent is the most important event, valued at a whopping 20 to 50 percent of scoring (the judging format undergoes change occasionally).

Other pageants that include a talent category include Miss Black America, the Cinderella system, Miss American Coed, and Miss Country USA. Many pageants offer talent as an optional event, or expand the guidelines beyond "stage talents." In America's Junior Miss, Miss T.E.E.N., and Miss Teen of America, entrants can perform a talent, demonstrate a skill or hobby, or give a speech.

What Judges Look For

Although the exact judging criteria differ depending upon the pageant and the specific talent, judges usually consider the following qualities:

- execution and skill
- technical difficulty
- confidence
- discipline and dedication
- facial expressions and on stage personality
- entertainment value and showmanship
- interpretation of the selection
- originality and creativity
- costuming and effective use of any props
- accuracy and recovery from mistakes
- choreography
- effectiveness of opening and finale
- the total impact of a performance

DEVELOP A WINNING TALENT

Whether or not you currently have a stage talent, read on. This chapter offers advice for everyone from the girl with "no talent" to the music major who's already a professional performer. The bottom line is, if you can come up with *something* to do in the talent competition, you double the number of contests you can enter—and increase the odds of eventually winning one of those crowns.

Whether it's a romantic classical piano performance, a rib-tickling ventriloquism routine, or a flashy show-gymnastics exhibit, an audience-pleasing talent is the quickest way to launch a contestant from the local runway to the national stage. That doesn't mean that a girl has to have years of talent lessons and performing experience. The talent competition is about *entertaining*. An unusual talent that fascinates the audience is just as likely to earn the judges' nod as a serious classical performance. But, whether you are a newcomer to the talent scene or a veteran performer using pageants for career exposure, you'll need to apply the three P's—planning, preparation, and practice—to put the crown within reach.

61 · Don't Let Lack of Talent Hold You Back

At first glance, talent seems to be the quality that either gains you points toward the crown or keeps you out of lucrative scholarship/talent pageants like America's Junior Miss and Miss America. "You've got to be realistic enough to realize that when talent is a large portion of the points, as in the Miss America program, you must have some degree of talent in order to participate," explains Dennison Keller, former producer of the Miss Ohio and Miss Texas telecasts. "If you don't have a talent, I think you need to look for another pageant without a talent competition or a pageant where there is a lesser emphasis on talent."

Unlike the Miss America program, where talent counts twice as much as the other categories, in other pageants like Miss T.E.E.N. and Teen of America, talent counts for only 15 to 20 percent of scoring. "If a girl is good in everything else, she could recite the alphabet backwards and pick up enough points to win," quips Warren Alexander, national director of the Miss Teen of America Pageant. "Of course, we expect them to have enough common sense to make themselves look as good as possible. It must be presented well. We've had archery, embroidery, and calligraphy, but they were wonderfully presented."

Such "talents" can reveal the real talent of being a great titleholder. "If the contestant is smart," says Warren, "during her talent presentation she'll show, 'Hey, I am capable of being Miss Teen of America. See how I handle myself onstage with this material.'"

Even in true "talent pageants," lack of a stage talent needn't prevent a girl from competing. According to Sam Haskell, senior vice-president of the William Morris Talent Agency, many young women who initially lacked talent developed stage talents in order to pursue the crown. "Talent has to be nurtured and acquired if it is not something you already have. A lot of girls who wanted to be Miss America had no talent when they first entered, but they found something they could do and worked at it, and worked at it, and worked at it." The skills they developed were simply tools to help them achieve their goals.

Debra Maffett, now a recording artist, is a classic example of a "croak-to-crown" talent-development saga. After being convinced by friends to enter her university's pageant, Debbie learned talent was required. She almost backed out at the last minute, but decided to try singing, although she had never sung for an audience. "I got up on stage and my worst fears were realized," she recalls. "I froze. My mind went blank. The words just didn't come out—in front of a thousand people!" When the pianist kept playing, Debbie hummed along, throwing in an occasional word. "I don't think I scored any talent points," she quips.

Such a fiasco would have quickly ended other beginners' pageant aspirations. Yet rather than quitting because she "didn't have talent," Maffett decided to build on her seemingly limited raw talent . . . at an age when other contestants were retiring from pageants. "Debbie had her first vocal lessons at age twenty-one," recalls her mother, Nonnie. "When she decided this was what she wanted, she just started doing it. During college, she would drive hundreds of miles to take voice lessons." Her determination paid off handsomely four years later. Debbie won a talent award and the Miss America title, proving to future contestants that lack of talent is not necessarily the end of the dream. Sometimes it's just the beginning.

62 · Get Training

Whether you're just beginning to explore your talent potential, as Debra Maffett did, or you're already an experienced performer, make every effort to improve your skills continually with proper training, particularly for the national level where many candidates are college music majors or professional entertainers. Such training is critical to developing impressive point-gaining techniques. "I don't think there is any substitute for training with experts in the field," asserts Dennison Keller, former producer/director of the Gillette Miss America Troupe and a state and national judge. "There is a direct correlation between the amount of training you have and how good your talent presentation is going to be. You can't ignore training. All those years of training are going to show."

Many Miss Americas had such formal training. Dorothy Benham ('77) and Susan Powell ('81) were vocal performance majors in college. Debra Barnes ('68) majored in piano while Tawny Godin ('76) studied piano at the Toronto Conservatory of Music. Gretchen Carlson ('89) had a decade of violin lessons and Marjorie Vincent ('91) had a bachelor's degree in music and had been a semi-finalist in the Stravinsky International Piano Competition. Each made the most of her training to capture her coveted title.

Quality training can help a contestant develop a talent even at a late stage in her pageant "career." Girls seeking to develop a stage talent quickly should bear in mind that it is easier to learn to sing in a limited time period than to master other musical skills. "It's easier to *develop* a vocal talent than it is an instrumental talent," says Keller. "An instrument takes years and years and years of practice, so you can't suddenly decide when you're eighteen that you want to play the piano in the Miss America Pageant. It just doesn't work that way. You would have to have several years before you could get a degree of difficulty acceptable for that level. But with vocalists, voices develop much later in life, so a lot of women don't know they have a voice until a music instructor at school or something says, 'Oh, you have a voice! Why don't you do a little solo here?,' and they're off and running."

Training can make such a great improvement to a young woman's talent that most state pageants now provide their winners with professional coaching to prepare for the nationals. "We seek outside help for her talent, with the preparation of talent tapes and with refining her presentation," explains Adair Brown, retired director of the Miss Colorado Pageant, which has produced numerous national winners and runners-up. "You don't have to be an expert in that talent, but you have to be professional in its presentation because that performance has to be of national quality."

63 · What If You Can't Afford Private Training?

Although private lessons are highly advisable, many students simply don't have the funds. Contestants whose budgets don't allow for private lessons will be reassured to learn that young women have won state and national titles as self-taught performers.

One such winner, former Miss Florida Kim Boyce, knows that with determination and constant practice, contestants can become skilled entertainers without professional training. "I tried one [vocal] class at a university and hated it," she recalls. "I just said, 'This isn't for me,' and I continued practicing on my own to develop my talent. I worked hard at it for many years." Kim's superb rendition of "The Rainbow Connection" vaulted her into the national semifinals and launched her career as a Christian recording artist.

Likewise, several Miss Americas won without benefit of expensive private training. Shirley Cothran and Marilyn Van Derbur taught themselves to play one selection on a musical instrument. Vonda Kay Van Dyke was a self-taught ventriloquist who practiced "on the job" at an amusement park. She performed twelve shows a day, six days a week, experimenting with hundreds of jokes and songs, and analyzing audience reactions. Her predecessor, Donna Axum, developed her voice performing with college musical groups. "I received a lot of training through school choirs and church choirs in the basics of voice projection, diaphramatic breathing, articulation, pronunciation, and proper facial expressions, all of which are wonderful tools which can be applied in everything from opera to pop."

The key to succeeding without expensive talent coaching, says Keller, is: "Even if you can't afford private training, find a vehicle in which to perform to build your confidence. [Miss America 1994] Kim Aiken's 'Summertime' was wonderful. She might not have had private training but she's mentioned that she sang in church Sunday after Sunday after Sunday. In school you can get extra training from your vocal music coach, your band coach, or the baton corps. There are ways of getting extra training. It doesn't have to be classical training or very costly training."

For new contestants who can't afford private lessons and feel intimidated competing against entrants who have had years of private training, local pageant director Jeff Bell advises: "Be confident in what you're doing and don't worry about the other contestants. Judges are looking for the best *overall*. While professionals who enter a pageant may be excellent in talent, they may be weak in other areas. The deciding factor is not who has the most professional talent—but who is the most well rounded and consistently strong contestant in every category."

64 · Dismiss the Idea That Only Singers Win

As novice contestants contemplate what type of talent to perform they are sometimes warned that singing is the only talent that wins. Is it true?

Although most judges evaluate nonvocal talents with an open mind, some judges are openly biased against nonsingers. Kaye Lani Rae Rafko, a dancer faced such discrimination at a state pageant when a veteran judge told her she'd have to switch to singing to win. Furious, Kaye Lani scolded the judge, refused to change her talent, and became the first Tahitian dancing Miss America. "The judges manual says that talent is based on creativity, uniqueness, stage presence, personality, and the training involved," she says. "It does not specify that you have to be a singer or instrumentalist. A talent is a talent."

Unfortunately, there is a widespread notion that singing is the only talent for a "serious" contestant. "There is a fallacy that you have to sing to win," says Sam Haskell, a renowned talent agent. "Everyone thinks that singing is the easiest thing to do . . . but it is also the easiest thing to do badly. The first thing I mark off on is a bad singer."

Haskell recommends that contestants avoid such pitfalls by focusing on their own strengths. "If a girl cannot sing well, I suggest that she find something that is unique to her—whether it's playing a musical instrument, doing a dramatic interpretation, dancing the hula, or playing 'Chopsticks' . . . as long as she does it well. It's better to do something that you already know how to do, feel comfortable doing, and do well, than to try to get up there and squeak out a song."

Like many girls, Shirley Cothran of Texas, once assumed she had to sing to win. After losing several times as a singer (including one loss to a roller skater), she switched to the flute—and won Miss America. Debbie Riecks, Miss Colorado 1989, told me that she too tried singing, then dumped it in favor of her stronger talent. "I sang when I first competed because I had the old traditional concept that you *had* to be a singer to win. Then I realized that it's not that you have to be a singer, but that you have to be able to communicate with the audience." She switched to the flute and, using a clip mike to move around the stage, performed "Dueling Banjos," "dueling" with an unseen banjo. The judges loved it and she placed as second runner-up to Miss America (who, incidentally, played the *marimba*). The key is it's got to be entertaining.

65 · The Secret to Selling Any Talent

The secret to "selling" any talent is showmanship. Any talent, if it is entertaining and performed well, can gain high scores.

Many contestants don't realize that pageants encourage entrants to present their own unique talents creatively. "I've seen pretty much anything," admits Robert Hedberg, director of programs for the America's Junior Miss Pageant. "We've seen the more traditional talents such as musical instrumentation or dance, but we have also had monologues, poetic readings, and demonstrations of art and personal works they have created. It's '*Creative* and Performing Arts.'"

Even the Miss America system, which is dominated by the traditional performing arts, has seen an increase in the variety of less-traditional talents. Today's judges appreciate that any talent that demonstrates skill and entertainment value can win. "When I was grooming Miss Ohios, we had two Miss Americas and several runners-up—but there was never a common denominator," explains Dennison Keller. "I had a five foot eleven belly dancer followed by a five foot one accordion player. One was first runner-up, the other was second runner-up [to Miss America]. That's how diverse they were. I think you can perform any talent as long as you do it well. Doing what you do *well* is the key."

Keep in mind that a superbly executed, entertaining nonvocal talent is statistically more likely to make the top ten than a singer. It is actually an advantage to be different, so do what *you* do well.

Many girls used nonvocal or unusual talents successfully in national competition:

(*) indicates she won the national title
(T) indicates the performance won talent

impersonations (T*)
floral arranging
trampoline (T*)
ballet (T*)
clogging
Chinese sword dance
swing dance (T)
driving a tractor (T)
horsemanship
comedy/mime (T)
chalkboard drawing
painting/sketching (T*)
sign language/poetry (*)
baton (T)
banjo (T)
accordion (T)
flute/saxophone (T*)
imitating Marilyn Monroe (*)
conduct pageant orchestra (T*)
karate/stomping in broken glass
roller-skating/ice skating (T)
ventriloquism/double-ventriloquism (T*)

puppeteer
furniture display
hula/Tahitian dancing (*)
tap dancing upside down
the Charleston (T)
South Sea dance (T)
tap dances (T)
gymnastics/acrobatics (T*)
contortionist act
archery (T)
magic act
spinet/organ (*)
drama/poetry (T*)
marimba (T*)
violin/fiddle (T*)
harp (*)
bass fiddle (T*)
fashion design exhibit (T*)
Russian cossack dance

films of water ballet and high-diving
middle eastern belly dancing
portrayal of Queen Elizabeth I in full costume (T*)
portrayal of *Romeo and Juliet* in period costume (T*)

Vernon DeSear, an expert national judge and performer with a background in voice and piano, affirms the appreciation for a variety of talents. "I have been thrilled by a wonderful ballerina, I've been impressed by a fabulous pianist, I've been overwhelmed by a wonderful singer, and I've been brought to tears by a good actress. I think they're *all* important. You know, talent runs the gamut," he says. "I don't think it matters *what* her talent is. The *girl* is still the one that wins it. Talent is just the icing on the cake."

66 · If You've Got Classical Talent—Flaunt It

Nonvocal and unusual talents can be very successful in competition, but few talents can rival the effectiveness of classical performances: vocal, instrumental, or dance. Although some so-called experts advise heavyweight classical performers to "tone it down" or switch to something the public can "relate" to . . . don't buy it. Quality classical talents are the surest way to leap from the local pageant stage to a national pageant telecast. "I love classical numbers," enthuses Kenn Berry, a veteran of four decades of judging. "I don't feel they're boring at all. God, no! I'm speaking strictly for myself, but to me, opera, classical ballet, and classical piano take a helluva lot to beat."

Berry is not alone in his appreciation for heavyweight talents. Classical performers have a superb record in talent pageants. Miss Americas Bess Myerson (1945), Neva Langley (1953), and Marjorie Vincent (1991) won talent trophies and the crown with classical piano, while Yolande Betbeze (1951), Dorothy Benham (1977), and Susan Powell (1981) were classical vocalists. Miss America 1989, Gretchen Carlson, was a classical violinist who had performed as a soloist with the Minnesota Orchestra, while America's Junior Miss for 1994, Amy Osmond (Marie's niece) was also a superb classical violinist.

Since some judges don't appreciate classical talents, showmanship is the key to making such performance more appealing. "Pick something that has some flash in it and some dramatic qualities, something that you can get into," recommends Kristin Huffman, a classical vocalist, national talent winner, and runner-up to Miss America 1990. "I think being a good actress is almost as important as how your voice sounds because a lot of people can't relate to opera. Get right in front of the judges and use your facial expressions. Just speak to them with your eyes," she says. "I think that is definitely what sells it."

The same applies to classical instrumental talents and classical dancers. "I think it can be harder to sell that," says Dennison Keller, a national judge and former producer of Miss Ohio and Miss Texas telecasts. "If you are a classically trained musician, there's worlds of wonderful, exciting symphonic pieces. If you're classically trained in ballet, dance to an exciting, vibrant, electrifying symphonic piece."

So, if you have a heavyweight classical talent, vocal, instrumental, or dance . . . don't play it safe. Make it entertaining and flaunt it.

67 · If You Don't Have Talent . . . Bluff

Sometimes, bluffing can help a gutsy contestant who lacks a stage talent. For instance, after being warned that her dramatic act wouldn't go over at the national pageant, Oklahoma's Jane Jayroe came up with a more flamboyant "talent"—conducting the pageant orchestra. She was voted Miss America 1967.

Her predecessor, Debbie Bryant, concocted a vaudeville spoof that she never dreamed might earn her the coveted crown. Without a stage talent, she decided to perform a melodrama with a heroine in distress, villain, and rescuing hero. As strobe lights flickered, Debbie performed all three roles by flapping around in a three-part costume. "I knew that my talent wasn't my strength," she quips. "You can't fall too much on your face when you're having fun, making a spoof out of it." The pageant's national director, Lenora Slaughter, wasn't as magnanimous. "I'll never forget," Bryant recalls, chuckling, "some of Lenora's first words to me were, 'Well, you won't ever have to do your talent again!'" But, the judges knew they had their winner the moment they met Debbie and they weren't going to lose her over a trivial matter of talent.

Similarly, two other ingenious contestants faked their way to the national throne by learning to play one song on a musical instrument. Texas's Shirley Cothran won her national title after memorizing one medley on the flute. During her reign she charmingly let the public in on her charade. "I'm not a flautist or a flutist," she'd admit with a giggle, "but a Texas flute-tooter. Because I can play the B-flat scale and one song—but I play it *very* well!"

Marilyn Van Derbur resorted to a similar strategy after her sorority drafted her into their school's local preliminary pageant. Faced with the requirement to perform a talent, she decided to try the organ because the judges couldn't compare it with anything else. When a friend composed a difficult-sounding but easy-to-play medley of "Tea for Two" and "Tenderly," Marilyn practiced four hours a day to memorize the pieces. Although it was the only tune she could play, it was sufficient to win her the local, state, and national titles.

However, Marilyn's first TV appearance after being crowned Miss America illustrates the dangers of bluffing. When she arrived for an appearance on *The Steve Allen Show*, the host complimented her on her organ performance the night before and mentioned that when they went on live coast-to-coast television in a moment she was to play another song, "Night and Day," for viewers. Luckily, Allen opted for a piano/organ duet and Marilyn survived the broadcast by smiling like mad and pretending to play along while Allen carried the tune!

So, while bluffing talent sometimes pays off, girls who do so should have a mental game plan for situations they may encounter if their bluff proves a tad *too* convincing.

CREATE A MOOD WITH MUSIC AND COSTUMING

To be successful, a talent performance must touch the hearts and emotions of the audience and judges. Whether your talent is a romantic classical piano selection, an exciting acrobatic routine, or a charming ventriloquist act, use music and costuming as tools to convey the theme of your performance and create a mood onstage.

68 · *The Secret to Winning Music for Nonsingers*

Good nonvocal talents have it made. Whether it's a dancer, musician, baton twirler, or gymnast, such talents are among the most likely performances to catch the judges' attention. Instrumentalists performing the piano, harp, flute, clarinet, saxophone, violin, fiddle, marimba, spinet, organ, and accordion have all made national finals or better, as have dancers performing ballet, acrobatic dances, tap, Tahitian, Hawaiian, middle eastern, cancan, and Polynesian dances, and the Charleston. In fact, *good* nonvocal talents are statistically slightly more likely to make national semi-finals than vocalists. Why? With over half of all entrants being singers, an entertaining musician or dancer simply stands out from the crowd.

But one of the secrets to "selling" such nonvocal talents is picking entertaining music that both the performer and her audience can enjoy. "I think audience appeal has ninety-nine percent to do with it," says Shirley Cothran, who emphasizes that when it comes to the talent competition, great music is the key to the crown. The music listings included in Tips #68 and #69 are the selections which statistically have the best track records in national talent competitions. All have been performed by national winners, finalists, semi-finalists, or talent winners.

Winning Music for Musicians

With any instrumental talent, familiar audience favorites are always a safe bet, particularly upbeat or romantic medleys on a "theme": Gershwin, patriotic, Dixie, country, Broadway, film overtures, TV theme songs, Hooked on Classics, Disney, Beatles, WWII–era, the fifties, love ballads, Miss America songs, etcetera.

For example, Shirley Cothran performed a lively flute medley of "Swingin' Shepherd Blues" and "Bumble Boogie" and Phyllis George won Miss America 1971 playing a piano medley of "Raindrops Keep Fallin' on My Head" and "Promises, Promises." Similarly, a banjo player won the national talent trophy plucking out "California, Here I Come," and "Alabamy Bound"; a saxophonist almost won Miss America playing "If He Walked into My Life" and "Yakety Sax"; and an accordionist nearly captured the national crown playing "Dizzy Fingers" and "Comedians' Gallop." Fiddlers regularly make the top ten playing "Czardias" and "Orange Blossom Special." Rock is also becoming popular. Miss Arkansas 1991 made the national semi-finals with her rousing piano/vocal performance of Jerry Lee Lewis's "Great Balls of Fire" ("Kiss me, baby!").

A musician's most valuable tool is fabulous music. Choose either beautiful romantic selections or catchy "clap-along" tunes to charm the audience and judges:

Night and Day	Embraceable You
With a Song in My Heart	Promises, Promises
Deep in the Heart of Texas	Memories
Star Dust	Through the Eyes of Love
Born Free	The Shadow of Your Smile
Misty	Someone to Watch Over Me
Ebb Tide	An Affair to Remember
Back Home Again in Indiana	Wabash Cannonball
There She Is, Miss America	The Swiss Shepherd Song
Theme from *Love Story*	Sunny/The Man I Love
Flight of the Bumble Bee	Shenandoah/Dueling Banjos
Bumble Boogie	

Winning Music for Dance/Baton/Acrobatics

The secret to winning with dance, baton, acrobatics, and other athletic talents is to infuse the performance with exciting choreography, clever costuming, and entertaining music that creates a catchy mood.

Contestants who succeeded with such talents "set" their performance to lively or moving musical selections. Miss America 1970 performed a ballet to *Romeo and Juliet*; while America's Junior Misses 1983 and 1977 danced *en pointe* to *Doll on a Toy Shell* and *Bless the Beasts and Children*. Several national finalists performed dance and acrobatics to "Singing in the Rain," and the theme from *Close Encounters of the Third Kind* and *Chariots of Fire*. Miss America 1979 won with a gymnastics routine to the theme from *Rocky* and "Feels So Good," while Miss New York 1979 won the national talent award and made top ten baton-twirling to "If They Could See Me Now."

To capture the audience and judges' attention, dance and athletic talents require music that is familiar, entertaining, and has a strong beat. Dramatic film overtures are especially effective.

Deep in the Heart of Texas	Hawaiian War Chant
Banjo Fantasy	Sleeping Beauty Waltz
Theme from "Ironside"	Grand Pas de Duex
Puttin' on the Ritz	Are You from Dixie?
Showstopper	Battle Hymn of the Republic
Overture from *Annie*	Overture from *Funny Girl*
Overture from *Oklahoma*	That's Entertainment
Theme from *Summer of '42*	Le Grande Holiday
Overture from *West Side Story*	Under the Bridges of Paris
Can-Can	

Winning Classical Music for Nonsingers

Classical performances are among the most successful talents of all, statistically. While they are considered more "serious" than other talents, they should never be less entertaining! Marian Cox, a piano and organ instructor with over thirty years of teaching experience and a decade of pageant involvement, recommends that classical musicians choose music that is both familiar and shows off different techniques. "Classical music played well is a winner every time," she says, rattling off several examples, "Grieg, Chopin, Rachmaninov, Ravel, Debussy. From beginning to end their music is really beautiful and showy." The best classical tunes catch audience interest and keep it. "A good piano piece makes you sit up and take notice right away," says Cox. "You don't want to wait until two minutes into the piece before you hear something exciting."

To impress judges with classical talents, perform familiar classics that are fun, emotionally stirring, or elegant:

Czardas	Warsaw Concerto
Toccata	Rhapsody in Blue
Fantaisie Impromptu	Gershwin's *Preludes*
Orange Blossom Special	Caprice Viennois
The Blue Danube	The Cadenza
Grieg's *Concerto*	Hora Stacato
Malaguena	Gypsy Airs
Summertime	Can-Can/Bumble Boogie
Flight of the Bumble Bee	Moonlight Sonata
Dr. Gradus ad Parnassum	Debussy's *Fireworks Prelude*
The Cat and the Mouse	

While classical music is highly successful in pageants, the music must be recognizable to the judges and audience. "There's the 'far out' music," Cox explains. "You can't tell if they're playing the right notes. Then there's the irregular rhythms in a lot of the contemporary music. Judges have a question in their minds: Was it completely right or not? Is there a real talent shown here? There's also the 'loud banging music' with banging from beginning to end . . . which just shows one thing," she quips. "You have powerful fingers! Fast tempos with fingers running up and down the keyboard certainly show off years of study and practice, but the *technique* has to be there." According to Cox, ideal classical music should feature various techniques:

- attention-commanding opening (arpeggios are ideal)
- recognizable melody
- correct balance between hands
- shading of loud and soft, fast and slow
- trills, arpeggios, and other impressive techniques
- use of the whole keyboard
- exciting ending (glissandos are always intriguing)

69 · The Secret to Winning Music for Singers

A singer's music must also be upbeat and audience-pleasing. Avoid songs with negative lyrics. Positive selections are far more appealing—and successful. "The 'torch song' is the best," asserts Steve Bishop, president of Express Trax, a leading pageant accompaniment tape firm. "The types of songs that are considered the stock pageant songs are the ballads like 'I am Changing,' 'I'll Be Home,' and 'Ain't Misbehavin'.' Songs in that vein are most popular. Although girls have done well with other style songs, the pop and Broadway ballads, the torch songs, seem to be the best."

With any winning vocal performance, strong emotional content is the winning ingredient. Torch songs and Broadway ballads are so appealing to judges because they invariably convey passion. "I think it's an emotional thing with the audience," suggests Bishop. "Some of them have a lot of emotion. They start soft and then build to a real big climax, where they hold long notes. It's the emotion."

The key to selecting winning music for any talent is: If the song gives you goose bumps the first time you hear it and delights you every time thereafter, it's a winner. I'll never forget the day I first heard the song "Don't Cry Out Loud." I was so moved that I turned to my fiancé and said, "That song will win Miss America one day." The following year Cheryl Prewitt performed it and walked off with the crown. You pick a winning song with your heart:

Ah, Je Veux Vivre	Night and Day
Una Voce Poco Fa	Don't Cry Out Loud
Care Nome	He Touched Me
Sempre Libera	Kiss Me in the Rain
Vissa D'Arte	I Am Changing
The Bell Song	You're My World
Un Bel Di	Come in from the Rain

'Ouando me'n vo'
Adele's Laughing Song
The Jewel Song
Jalousie
Habanera
Lucie's Aria/Hello, Hello
Summertime
This Is My Beloved
My Heart at Thy Sweet Voice
Mira
There'll Come a Time

All the Things You Are
A New Life
Crazy
Golden Rainbow
On My Own
A Piece of Sky
I Dreamed a Dream
As Long As He Needs Me
Wind Beneath My Wings
Stormy Weather

Reflect Your Personality

Whether the performance is a torch song or aria, the music should reflect the contestant's personality. For instance, having survived a horrible auto accident in childhood and doctors' prognosis that she would never walk again, Cheryl Prewitt wanted to perform music that reflected her optimism and victory over tragedy. She chose "Don't Cry Out Loud," because, she recalls, "I wanted a song which was very uplifting, something about goals and dreams, which is what my life has always been. It was a great song for *me*." Terry Meeuwsen, Miss America 1973, selected the stirring song "He Touched Me" to express the impact becoming a Christian had made upon her life. Similarly, Leanza Cornett chose a song that voiced the message of her AIDS education and prevention platform. Her stirring performance of "A New Life" ("What would I give to have a new life?") gave our panel goose bumps.

Not Overused

Keep in mind that once someone has won with a musical selection it is relentlessly copied. Judges eventually tire of the song and it loses its winning edge. Always keep an ear "tuned" for songs that have graduated from success to saturation. "Contestants should look for a song that hasn't been used and used and used in pageants," advises Cheryl Prewitt-Salem, "something that is going to be refreshing for listeners."

Avoid overly familiar songs—unless your voice is as good as the original artist. "I know you're not supposed to compare them with the recording, but it's very difficult at times not to compare them," says Roger Knight, a pageant judge and former Miss Florida official. "If we've heard it played countless times on the airwaves—when you hear someone else sing it, it's just not quite as good. I think it's a bad choice for a girl to pick a very famous song or a very recent hit unless she can do it extremely well and really sell it."

Right for the Voice

The music should be right for the voice. The right note range for the contestant's level of skill is imperative. Every song has a different range of notes, from a narrow range to a very wide range. A singer or musician must be able to perform the complete range of notes in her music. If she can't, if the song requires too much of a stretch, she will lose points. Music teachers and choral directors can help entrants determine their correct vocal range. Novices should select songs with a limited range of notes well within their ability, while advanced performers should show off their superb skills with more challenging selections. Taped accompaniment is available in every vocal range.

I cannot overemphasize how important the right music is to a contestant's chances. After judging Leanza Cornett at the Miss America Pageant, I viewed a tape of her winning talent performance at the Miss Florida Pageant. Despite the fact that Leanza was already a professional singer and performer at Disney MGM Studios, her rendition of "With One More Like You" at the state level was fine but not dazzling. Yet less than three months later, when she performed a different selection, "A New Life," at the national pageant, several of the judges awarded her perfect tens. Same voice, same degree of vocal development—yet one performance left me cold while the other gave me goose bumps. Why? Leanza's musical selection for the nationals was flawless for *her*, evoking powerful emotions and perfectly suiting her voice and AIDS platform.

Picking the right music is one of the most important decisions a contestant will make. The "right" music should create a winning image by fitting her age, personality, and level of skill, and by entertaining the audience and judges.

70 · Sound Like a Pro With a Sound Track

With talent often counting for a hefty chunk of scoring, a talent performance should be as professional as possible. Most pageants now require taped background music to simplify production. Fortunately, prerecorded accompaniment music is one of the most effective—and least expensive—steps a contestant can take to improve her presentation. Starting at $15 each, music tracks are affordable. They also make timing a cinch. Music tracks are preedited to fit the time requirements of each system, so whatever pageant a girl is entering, music is available in the right time limit.

With affordable, pretimed, high-tech help available, singers and musicians should avoid performing to a single instrument accompaniment—either onstage or on tape. It looks and sounds amateurish. "Unfortunately, a lot of girls have done that, not knowing that good tracks are available," says Steve Bishop, president of Express Trax, a top pageant music-track firm. "They've gotten Grandma to play somethin' on the old upright, taped it on a cheap tape-recorder, and they turn it in. I've seen it many a time. It's unfortunate for the girl," he continues, "because she could have a much better track, a full orchestra backing her up for very little money." The orchestra sound provided by prerecorded tracks adds excitement and professionalism to a talent performance. "A lot of the emotion and saleability of the song comes from the music, no matter how good a singer you are," says Steve, "so get the best track you can."

In addition to making a talent performance sound more professional, a quality track also helps the young woman to be comfortable with her music. "The big advantage of using a track is, you know the arrangement, you've learned the track, you know how the music is going to go," explains Bishop. "You can play it in your car, at home—anywhere. You can practice with the song and know it up and down. Those girls who haven't had much entertainment experience can practice and practice and practice, and learn that one song very well. That's a big advantage." For practice, pageant tracks feature a for-performance side, an instructional demo side, and a lyrics sheet for memorization. "When you flip the tape over there is a demonstration vocal," says Steve, "so they can play the demo side and learn the song, then flip it over and have their music without the vocal."

Never get onstage to perform without having practiced with the tape. One local entrant learned that lesson the hard way. She purchased a track of a hit tune she often sang along with on the radio, and without practicing with the tape, she went onstage to perform it. To her horror, she discovered in front of the judges that the taped version was in a different key and she *couldn't* sing it. Always practice with your music tape before performing it in competition.

Finally, keep a backup tape. If the original music track breaks, you don't want to find yourself out on a technicality. Keep a spare.

71 · Set the Mood With Your Talent Costume

While the right music and a good sound track can help you sound like a winner, costuming is another effective tool for crafting a winning talent performance. "I look for appropriate costuming," affirms John Moskal, a veteran judge and actor known for his roles on *Knots Landing* and *Days of Our Lives*. "In talent, if a contestant is trying to create a mood, an ambiance onstage, her costuming helps to show that. Wardrobe choices are crucial," he advises. "Just as crucial as her music piece."

Reflect Your Music

Ideally, costuming should set the mood of the talent for judges. "The talent is all show business," says Thomas Tolbert of Legends, pageant clothing specialists. "Entertain me! The costuming depends on the song [the contestant] is going to play, but for the classics I always see something in black or white, something very symphonic-looking. Gershwin is a little more showy, so she needs to have a little more sparkle and glitz. If a young lady is going to do opera, I see her in full operatic dress with that flowing look so she can be dramatic with her hands. Now if a girl is doing Christian sacred music, I'd put her in white or a soft pastel to look angelic and pure."

Mixing images can wreak havoc on a talent performance. For example says Tolbert, "If she's playing 'Great Balls of Fire' and she's in white chiffon—she's going to look stupid." Make sure the costuming conveys the image of the music. He chuckles, recalling one real-life near-miss. "One girl came in and said she wanted to wear red for her talent." Fine—except that she intended to sing the Christian classic, "Amazing Grace." "I said, 'No you can't *do* that, because somehow 'Amazing Grace' in red does not make a whole picture." Costuming should match the genre and mood of the music.

(LEGENDS)

"Talent costuming should set the mood of the performance for the judges," says Thomas Tolbert, of Legends.

Costuming for Singers

A singer's costuming should instantly convey the mood of her musical selection. "We try to work the talent outfit around the whole song," explains Robin Elliott-Bear, of Robin Elliott Ltd. She cites the example of a state finalist whose costuming helped create an aquatic mood for her performance of *The Little Mermaid*. "We did a sequin dress that was royal blue and turquoise and she *looked* like the Little Mermaid. She was a great actress with a pretty good voice—but her 'total package' made you feel like you were in the water with her while she sang."

Classical singers should convey a suitably theatrical mood with operatic attire. Historical themes are ideal: regal colors, rich velvets, period styling, bouffant sleeves, full skirts, and dramatic trains . . . topped off with glitz. One of the secrets to selling opera is wearing a spectacular costume that gets—and keeps—judges' attention. Never sing classical music in a contemporary beaded gown.

A more contemporary singer's costuming should be an extension of her music. Rebecca King, Miss America 1974, set the mood for "If I Ruled the World" with a regal scarlet velvet gown encrusted with rhinestones. Leanza Cornett, an AIDS prevention advocate, used symbolism in her choice of attire. She performed the tearjerker, "A New Life," clad in a pure white gown accented with a blood-red AIDS ribbon. In each case, the singer's costuming conveyed the theme of her music and created a specific "mood" onstage.

Costuming for Musicians

When choosing your costume or designing one, keep in mind the unique demands of the talent.

For instance, a pianist is usually positioned so judges can watch the keyboard, which hinders a girl's ability to "connect" with the panel. "Often the judges will be seated so they can't

(PAUL ABEL)

Classical vocalist Kimilee Bryant, Miss South Carolina 1989.

see anything but the back, so you'll want to have back inter-est," says Thomas Tolbert. "If she is going to be at an angle, get some interest to draw the eye up to her face. Hands are impor-tant too, but you want to see the *face*."

(IRV KAAR)

Classical pianist Majorie Vincent, Miss America 1991.

Successful looks for pianists include gowns with tailored or flowing trains and eye-catching detailing on the torso, shoulders, and sleeves. Marjorie Vincent (1991) chose a simple black skirt with a red-and-black embroidered tulip train. Kellye Cash, Miss America 1987, opted for a fitted black gown with sequin artwork across the shoulders and back.

Since wind and string musicians use facial expressions, hand motions, and movement around the stage to project personality, they must use costuming to focus attention on those areas. Detailing on the bodice, neckline, shoulders, and sleeves helps draw attention to the performer's face and instrument. "Put the artwork at the bodice going up," advises Tolbert. "If you have the artwork at the top it draws your attention up to her face." Chiffon, taffeta, or velvet skirts, and understated tone-on-tone beaded skirts are all suitable bottoms.

Musicians with energetic numbers should select costuming that compliments body movements. Miss Missouri 1983, a fiddler, won a national talent award wearing a fully fringed pantsuit that swayed in unison with her lively performance.

Costuming for Dancers / Athletic Talents

Physically demanding talents such as dance, baton, and acrobatics require outstanding costuming that defines the mood of the performance. Whether it's classical or modern ballet, a sultry jazz number, glamorous Hollywood-style tap, seductive island dance, or energetic acrobatic act, proper costuming can add professionalism and instantly intrigue the audience and judges.

Consider the attention-getting costuming used by several national semi-finalists. From the moment Sandy Frick, a ballerina famous for moon-walking *en pointe* to "Yankee Doodle Dandy," leaped onstage in toe shoes, colonial military hat, and Revolutionary War "uniform," judges knew there wouldn't be any dying swans in her performance. Miss Alabama 1993 performed an acrobatic dance in a harem costume and "I Dream of Jeannie" hairdo; Miss Massachusetts 1992 performed a can-can *en pointe* in a Parisian chorus-girl costume; and Miss Ohio 1978 shimmied in a seductive harem costume for her tradition-breaking belly dance. Furthermore, Kaye Lani Rae Rafko became the first Tahitian dancer to win a major title after she slinked onstage attired in a low-riding pink grass skirt, strapless bustier, and towering feather headdress. Needless to say, no one had to nudge the judges awake. Use costuming to get—and keep—the judges' attention.

Whether the contestant is a dancer, baton twirler, musician, or singer, her costuming should instantly establish the genre of her performance for the judges and develop a specific mood onstage. "You have to create an image," advises Stacy King, Miss

Louisiana 1989, a spirited banjo player. "Everything has to fit. Everything has to be perfect. The total picture is the key." Just as a gown "tells" judges who a woman is, a talent costume also conveys a specific image. What "message" will your costuming send judges?

LEARN TO PERFORM LIKE A PRO

While the right music and costuming establishes the mood of a talent, successfully selling a performance to the judges and audience requires experience. Repeatedly performing onstage (and surviving a few flubs in the process) trains a contestant to be confident with thousands of eyes upon her, handle a microphone comfortably, keep her cool when something goes wrong onstage, and project showmanship across the footlights. The more experience a contestant gains performing, the more confident and professional her performance becomes in the spotlight of competition.

72 · Gain Experience Performing

The easiest way to develop a stage talent is to take small steps to gain experience before an audience. Over time, many "steps" of experience performing in front of an audience can nurture a fledgling talent into a mature, confident performance.

"It's important to make yourself get out and perform in public," advises Christina Chriscione, a former Miss New Jersey, "even if it's just at your local church. Get that experience. As corny as it sounds, stand there and perform in front of your family—just like your mom made you do when you were a kid," she chuckles. "As a singer you're opening up your heart and soul, and unless you've had some experience, it's a frightening thing to 'let go.' You have a tendency to become introverted when you don't feel comfortable. That's the last thing you can afford to do when you're performing. You need to get experience performing."

Even small towns offer opportunities to perform: church services, birthday parties, school musicals, nursing homes, civic clubs, political events, holiday programs, talent contests, local pageants, and so on. By accepting increasingly challenging opportunities to perform, a new performer steadily increases her confidence.

"You have to *do* it to be good at it," advises Kim Boyce, a Christian recording artist and semi-finalist at the 1983 Miss America Pageant. "I really think years of standing onstage is what develops stage presence. Whether your talent is singing, baton twirling, gymnastics, or whatever, you have to keep doing it to become good at it. If you haven't had a lot of experience you just have to force yourself to go out there onstage, no matter how nervous you are, no matter how much you think you're going to mess up. Just go ahead and *do* it—and know that you're gaining valuable experience in the process."

To gain experience with a vocal talent, Steve Bishop, of Express Trax, recommends that singers consider purchasing a karaoke, what he calls "a sing-along machine that's basically a portable public address system." This lightweight, high-tech machine features two cassette players, speakers, a microphone, and some special effects. It is an ideal tool for a contestant to practice her talent, master microphone technique, and record herself performing with her background music. To gain experience performing, she can also bring it to public appearances where audio equipment is unavailable. Gain experience any way you can.

73 · Practice, Practice, Practice

Getting up onstage and gaining experience as a performer is invaluable, but what actually prepares contestants for those public performances are the hours of practice they invest before stepping onstage to perform. Whatever the talent, practicing helps contestants feel comfortable onstage and to perform with that wonderful quality of apparent effortlessness.

Even seasoned professionals rely on practice. Terry Meeuwsen, Miss America 1973, who was already a performer with the New Christy Minstrels, perfected her skills with constant practice. "Whenever we were with someone who had never heard me sing, Ginny [Virginia Habermann, her coach] would say, 'Terry . . . 'He Touched Me.' I was expected to sing it as though I were selling it to nine judges in Atlantic City. I sang a cappella everywhere you could conceive of. I sang in hair salons. I sang in restaurants. I sang on street corners. I sang in dress shops. I would be singing in the middle of a store while people were wandering around shopping. When I look back on it I think I must have been out of my mind to have done those things! But I'll tell you, it really paid off for me."

Shirley Cothran is another example of how diligent practice can work wonders in shaping up even the puniest talent. Although she had been dabbling with the flute for years, Cothran hadn't been able to afford private lessons. But she refused to let her limited training hold her back. What she didn't have in professional coaching, she simply made up for in practice. "It became such a part of me because I practiced it every day," she explains. "Maybe not in one sitting, but every time I had an extra five minutes or two minutes and fifty seconds, I would play my song until I absolutely could play it backwards."

"When you get on that stage, you have to be extremely comfortable with what you're doing and confident," Cothran warns, "because when you get out there, and all of a sudden you're not thinking of the music or fingering the different notes—but you're praying, 'Lord, help me to get through this piece without stumbling'—it needs to be *automatic*. That's extremely important for contestants. You only have one chance to play that song," she says. "You may have played it flawlessly fifty times before that, but if you make a mistake that one time, that's the only chance you get. So, it's important to have it down perfectly."

Investing in practice can pay off in unexpected, life-changing benefits. When Donna Axum competed for the Miss Arkansas title, she and another contestant were tied for the state crown. Organizers asked the judges to break the tie by determining which of the women had earned the most points in talent. Donna had earned two more points. By that sliver of a margin, she was named Miss Arkansas and went to the nationals where she won the national crown. "Imagine being that close to a life-changing experience," Donna exclaims. "That should be an example that you should practice an extra hour or two to get that one-point, two-point edge—because it can really make the difference."

Practice, practice, practice.

74 · Handle a Microphone Like a Pro

The right microphone is important for a successful talent performance. "Whether it is a microphone for a gal singing a classical piece or for someone playing the piano, the microphone should be part of the total presentation, just like a costume or anything else," advises Dennison Keller, former producer of the Miss Ohio and Miss Texas telecasts.

Microphones are especially important for singers. Stand microphones, corded hand mikes, and wireless hand mikes are all used in competition, but most state and national pageants now use quality wireless hand mikes.

Mastering microphone technique is critical to effective performance with any hand mike. It's important to position the mike in front of the mouth at all times to avoid an "evaporated" voice. Also avoid screaming into the microphone during long notes. You don't want to have your judges cringing in pain. When increasing your volume, shift the mike away from your mouth slightly. Dennison Keller advises new performers to practice with microphones in a school auditorium. "You have to practice with a microphone to develop microphone technique. You develop that by listening to yourself. You'll know when you're singing too loudly or too softly, and you learn to adjust it accordingly."

Further, says Keller, "If you use a hand-held mike, it's got to be choreographed. You need to know where you're going on that stage and what hand should be on the microphone at all times. You don't want to always have the microphone in one hand, or always use the same gestures. Use the right hand for a while, use the left hand for a while, and gesture with each hand. You've got to choreograph it just as a dancer choreographs her performance."

Classical and semi-classical singers should use stand microphones because they create a suitably elegant appearance and allow the singer to concentrate on proper diaphragm support. "I don't think you would use anything other than a stand mike with a classical or even semi-classical number," advises Keller. One recent state contestant performed a classic aria with a hand mike, moving around the stage in Broadway torch-song style. It was a distracting image mismatch. Use a stand mike, appropriate facial expressions, and graceful hand movements to create a suitably stately aura for a semi-classical performance.

String or wind instrumentalists can either use a stand microphone with a boom, or if they prefer to move around the stage as they perform, a clip-mike can be attached onto their instrument.

Whatever your talent, practice with the microphone you will use in competition.

75 · Turn Talent Disasters Into Victory

Falling flat on her face during the talent competition is a contestant's worst nightmare, but it can also be her best teacher.
Failures are great building blocks to success because they show
contestants what *not* to do the next time. If you use talent mistakes as a teacher, those "failures" can bring you closer to the
crown.

Since onstage disasters do arise, every competitor should be
mentally prepared to handle a major mistake should one occur.
Never let a mistake shake your concentration—continue with
your performance. And remember the remarkable example of
Sandy Frick, who turned calamity into a crown. During the
preliminaries at the 1989 Miss Florida Pageant, Sandy, a superb
dancer and favorite for the title, fell during her character ballet *en pointe*. Never having fallen onstage before, she was
stunned, but recovered instantly, leaping to her feet to continue her difficult performance.

Then, when Sandy made the finals, she slipped and fell on
live television. She sprang to her toes like a champion and
completed her performance masterfully. A lesser competitor
would have given up, but Sandy used the setback to prove she
had the unshakable composure of a champion. She was awarded the Miss Florida title that night and later made the top ten
at Miss America. "The most important thing is to show them
that you can handle any situation," advises Sandy. "It can happen to anybody. You never know, so you have to be *ready* for
the unexpected all the time." If you have an onstage blunder,
"Don't let it get you down," she says. "Just pick yourself back
up and say, 'I can do it, I have to keep going, I can't give up.'"
Her experience illustrates how maintaining composure in the
midst of a talent crisis can help put the crown within your
reach.

The most common crises involve microphones. If your mike

goes dead during your performance, don't allow the distraction to fluster you. Don't stop singing. First, unobtrusively check the microphone to see if its switch is off. If so, calmly turn it back on. If there is a technical problem with the mike, continue performing, even if the audience can't hear you. The audio crew will be rushing to correct the problem. Usually they can do so quickly, so watch for signals. If a technical problem can't be corrected, someone will walk onstage and hand you a new mike. Accept it and continue performing without pausing, although a quick nod or smile of appreciation is fine.

When faced with such a microphone malfunction, view the problem as an opportunity to gain points for composure under pressure. "The judges are looking for a girl who can handle any situation," explains Cheryl Prewitt-Salem, who won her national title after surviving a microphone problem during her talent performance. "I think it made a big impression that I just went on and acted like nothing was wrong," she observes. "Judges are looking for a girl who can handle a crisis, a girl who can handle an uncomfortable situation."

In fact, judges will often award bonus points to someone who maintains her composure during an onstage problem, so view such incidents as an opportunity. Finally, remember that judges are instructed to "focus on the things over which the contestant has control." And the one thing you always have control over is *your response*. Always keep your cool.

76 · Win With Showmanship

Personality and showmanship are keys to the hearts—and votes—of judges. The personality a contestant projects from beginning to end of her performance plays a decisive role in her appeal to judges. "Without showmanship your talent's not going to work," asserts Robert Zettler, past president of the Miss Ohio Pageant. "It may mean making someone come to tears, or fall down with laughter, or feel good—but they'd better create some *emotion*."

From the moment you walk onstage, project the charisma and confidence of a pro. "They have to think of themselves as *entertainers*," Zettler stresses, "not just as somebody presenting a talent. They have to take that audience and say, 'I *own* you for the next two minutes and fifty seconds and I am going to command your attention.'" He advises new contestants, "Visualize yourself as an entertainer. You're doing a full concert in two minutes and fifty seconds. You have to have a good beginning, no letdown in the middle, and a grand finale. Leave them wanting more."

Projecting personality can be difficult for instrumentalists who are limited to facial expressions, their song's audience appeal, and their movement onstage to "connect" with judges. "I'll tell you, it's tough," admits Stacy King, Miss Louisiana 1989, who performed a banjo medley to win her state title. "You have to learn how to sell it! It's much easier to sell a vocal talent where you can speak and relate to the audience, than it is for an instrumentalist to sell her talent. With the banjo you have to relate with your eyes and your facial expressions. Doing that plus your movements onstage is a little tough. Choreography is also a big part of it, just getting the right moves and picking the right songs. Pick something familiar that the audience has heard before, like 'Dueling Banjos' or 'Foggy Night Breakdown'."

Projecting personality to the audience can also be more challenging for dancers. "I think it's hard with dancers because there's not as much communication between the judges and the contestant," explains Miss California 1989, Wendy Berry, a ballerina and student of behavioral psychology. "A singer can communicate, she can look at the judges. But as a dancer, I can't spot them and sit there and look at them while I'm dancing, because it will throw me, so I think there's a lack of communication. But I love classical ballet and I try to have that come through to the audience and judges."

Developing showmanship is even more important when the girl is not especially gifted in her field. "You have to have personality," advises Dorothy Benham, Miss America 1977, "and if you're *not* a tremendous talent you have to sell it—no matter *what* you do. Whether you're a pianist, a dancer, a singer, or an actress, you have to be able to relate that to that audience. Show them the personality inside of you and draw them into whatever you're doing."

Project personality throughout your performance and as you conclude. Your finale is the panel's last glimpse of you before they award you a score. Infuse those final moments in front of the judges with energy and showmanship. Stay "in character" until you are completely offstage. A serious classical singer should curtsy and glide behind the curtain with the dignity of a Metropolitan diva. The effervescent clogger should almost bounce offstage. The ballerina's departure should radiate grace. The gymnast or baton twirler's exit should exude energy. Your exit is the "signature" to your performance.

Showmanship is the quality that transforms a fine performance into a winning talent.

SEVEN

The Winning Evening Gown

Sell yourself as an individual in an elegant situation.
REX HOLT, GUYREX ASSOCIATES

A s the most glamorous event in pageantry, the evening gown competition provides entrants with an ideal opportunity to look their most beautiful, project the image of a winner, and clinch the crown.

Like the other events, evening gown competitions differ. Beauty pageants like Miss USA, Miss Universe, Miss Teen USA, Miss Teen All American, Mrs. America, and GuyRex's Miss United States (formerly Miss World-America) emphasize beauty, glamour, fashion, charisma, and poise.

Scholarship pageants usually emphasize classic beauty, elegance, grace, and poise. The Miss America program's evening wear competition now downplays glitz and permits a wider range of formalwear. The America's Junior Miss Pageant conducts "Presence and Composure," a choreographed group routine in formalwear, while the Miss T.E.E.N. and Miss Teen of America pageants judge entrants individually in formal presentation categories that emphasize a wholesome teen image.

What Judges Look For

While the specific image of each pageant's evening gown competition and the exact judging criteria will differ, some of the qualities judges consider include:

- first impressions
- beauty of face and figure
- poise, presence, and composure
- appropriate image for the pageant
- appropriate for her age
- personality projection and charisma
- if the gown and girl compliment each other
- posture, carriage, walk, modeling technique
- grace and composure under pressure
- proper fit
- naturalness, youthfulness, grooming
- good taste (is the gown too suggestive?)
- overall appearance

THE PERFECT EVENING GOWN

To convince the judges that she is their winner, a contestant must *look* like a winner. To score highly she must develop grace and confidence of bearing and select eveningwear that flatters her figure, compliments her hair and skin tones, reflects her personality, makes her feel like a queen, and creates a total winning image.

77 · Carry Yourself Like a Queen

A winning look in the evening gown competition requires that a young woman present herself elegantly onstage. Her carriage is especially important since judges score each contestant on how graceful, poised, and composed she appears. "It's how well she can move, carry herself, and present herself in the formalwear of her choice," explains Rex Holt, of GuyRex's Miss United States.

The way a young woman walks is one of the first—and most important—qualities the panel will observe during the evening gown competition. "We look for class and elegance," says Richard Guy, also of GuyRex Associates. "The most important thing is elegance. Let's say a girl is absolutely gorgeous," he offers. "Then you see her modeling onstage and she walks like a truck driver. Well, out she goes! She can't move." Unfortunately, the importance of a regal walk is often overlooked by new contestants. "When I start working with girls who are entering their first pageant, they all walk the runway like they're going to a five-alarm fire," says Thomas Tolbert, of Georgia's Legends. "They're uncomfortable and they want to get on and off fast. But they've got to take their time, they've got to look elegant."

Fortunately, a beautiful walk can be developed, according to former Miss America Laurel Schaefer, who is famous for her regal bearing. "Your walk, particularly in your gown, should look like you are on rollers, that someone at the end of the runway has you on coasters and they're pulling you down the runway. You should literally glide. There should be no bouncy movement." Laurel recommends the classic "book-on-your-head" method for perfecting posture. "You learn where your center of gravity is and it pulls the spine correctly." Shorter steps also help. "Many girls just take too big a step, and everybody is looking at their feet. . . . The secret of a beautiful walk is first of all to have a wonderful, radiant smile so that what people are really looking at is your face. Take the attention away from your feet."

Never underestimate how your carriage, posture, and walk can create a winning—or losing—image. Carry yourself like a queen.

78 · *Create the Right Image for the Pageant*

Image is everything in evening gown. The gown is simply the tool to create the right image to project to the judges. Since each pageant's "look" is different, an evening gown should convey the image of the system a contestant is entering. "There is a definite 'look' for each pageant," explains Kathleen Munson, a pageant consultant and owner of The Pageant Shop.

Beauty Pageants

In beauty pageants like Miss USA, Miss Universe, Mrs. America, and GuyRex's Miss United States, the evening gown 'look' is unquestionably glamorous and fashionable. "Ours is more high fashion," says Richard Guy. "Wear whatever your style is." Aim to look so stunningly beautiful that you take the judges' breath away. Curve-hugging gowns in luxurious crepes, beaded fabrics, French laces with crystal, sparkling brocades, gold or silver metallics, or rich velvets trimmed with rhinestones have all been worn with success. Designs that would be too sensual for scholarship pageants often work well in true beauty pageants, as demonstrated by the five recent Miss USAs who wore sexy "Jessica Rabbit" strapless beaded gowns. Go for the glamour.

Scholarship/Family-Emphasis Pageants

Contrary to the glamorous image beauty pageants are noted for, scholarship pageants are attempting to put aside their "walking chandelier" look and cultivate an elegantly understated, classically beautiful image. The Miss America program has renamed its evening gown competition, "evening wear competition," and entrants are asked to avoid overly ornate gowns. "With Miss America, the emphasis is now on fabric rather than beading," notes Munson. "We're seeing tulle, chiffon, georgette, better crepes, and velvets. I think we're going back to that look of elegance." The first winner selected under the new guidelines, Kimberly Aiken, wore a simple, but elegant, black gown without a bead on it. It was the first unbeaded gown in a decade and the first simple black gown to win in a half a century. Yet she still projected the classically beautiful image that title exemplifies. "Mrs." pageants emphasizing marriage and family values usually follow trends in Miss America.

Teen Pageants

To project the right image for teen pageants, formalwear should be appropriate for the age. Competitions for teens, like Cinderella, Young Miss of America, and Universal Southern Charm, expect contestants to wear floor-length dresses that convey a suitably youthful, wholesome image. "Keep them innocent as long as you can," advises Beverly McGinn, of Grandma's Angels, specialists in pageant attire for younger contestants. "For heaven's sake, they're all in these sexy gowns when they're older." Gowns in white and pastels in soft fabrics like chiffon, tulle, georgette, satin, and sometimes velvet, are popular, with lace trims, pearl or bead embroidery, dainty necklines, puffed or ruffled sleeves, peplums, and gathered or tiered skirts. "Try to keep them young and fresh," says McGinn.

Teen scholarship programs prefer simple, clean-cut, youthful, floor-length dresses. The America's Junior Miss look is usually described as "debutante." "Our requirements last year were that we were not looking for the 'mermaid' dresses with all the beading," explains Robert Hedberg, director of programs, "but something fitting for their age. The last couple of years in Presence and Composure we've been utilizing the traditional white dresses." Guidelines for the Miss Teen of America Pageant (ages thirteen to eighteen) require, "simply styled and unadorned gowns." According to Warren Alexander, national director,

(MISS TEEN OF AMERICA/PAGEANT FOTO, INDIANAPOLIS, INDIANA)

A gown should convey the right image for that pageant. Unlike glamorous "beauty pageants," the Miss Teen of America scholarship pageant's look is simple and wholesome.

"Judges seem to prefer something very simple, youthful, and wholesome. The last few years we've seen a little rhinestone or sequin trim, but very, very slight." In both systems, satin, taffeta, velvet, and chiffons are popular choices. The Miss T.E.E.N. Pageant (ages thirteen through eighteen) also encourages a wholesome look, but moderately beaded dresses are often seen and the national winners in 1991 through 1993 wore beaded gowns modeled after those worn at Miss America.

In teen beauty pageants like Miss Teen USA and Miss Teen All American, gowns can be a bit glitzier. Yet, a too-mature look can backfire. "I will take points off if a gown is inappropriate for a certain age group," asserts John Moskal, a veteran state and national judge and television actor. "I don't want to see a teen contestant trying to look like she's twenty-five. She should look wholesome and every bit a teenager. Even in the USA program, if you put a Miss USA contestant next to a Miss Teen USA contestant, you should see a difference. If not, there's something wrong." In fact, while many teen contestants go for the glitz, most Miss Teen USAs have worn simple, pretty styles: ('88) Mindy Duncan, dainty white ruffles; ('90) Bridgette Wilson, simple magenta satin; ('92) Jamie Solinger, feminine green chiffon; ('93) Charlotte Lopez, unbeaded magenta brocade.

Although the gown is not officially judged, the image a contestant creates in that gown reveals what personal style she would bring to the title, and can set her apart as the obvious winner. "In evening gown you're really trying to culminate the total process of judging," explains Vernon DeSear, an expert on judging methods. "You're asking yourself, 'Is this the right girl for the job? Does this girl present the picture that we want to represent us?' She needs to project the total composite picture of what that title is all about." Reflecting the right picture in evening gown can help a young lady look like she *could* be that pageant's titleholder. Create the right image for the pageant.

79 · Make Your Gown a "Portrait" of Your Personality

The ideal gown will also complement the young lady's personality by highlighting her best qualities. She is painting her "portrait" for the panel. And, as any artist knows, a Rembrandt is different from a Rubens. Yet both are masterpieces. The same principle applies to evening gowns. A girl's evening gown "portrait" should be her masterpiece—beautiful and individual. "When you are judging evening gown, you are judging her overall look," says Debbie Brown, of Brides & Beauties, who dressed Miss USA 1994 and Miss America 1994 for evening gown competition. "You're not judging whether you like her dress. You're judging how this dress looks on her. Does it show her off well? Does it complement her personality? You are not judging the dress."

However, judges *do* consider what that gown says about a young woman's suitability to be their winner. The moment she steps onstage, a contestant's gown style and color reveal volumes about her personality (is she reserved or flamboyant?), attitude (does she like to command respect or shock?), and image (is she a Grace Kelly, a Marilyn Monroe, or a Tonya Harding?). Obviously, a red sequin dress with the plunging neckline is going to send judges an entirely different message than the flowing pink-lace-and-chiffon number.

Getting that message right is critical. To avoid sending mixed signals to judges a girl's personality should influence the choice of gown. "If you have someone who is a very confident, flamboyant personality, she can wear something that is flashier than a young woman who is demure," explains Tricia Copelin, of Mississippi's Custom Creations By Tricia. "Sometimes you have a girl who is bubbly, a cheerleader type, and other times you have a girl who is elegant, high-fashion, and sophisticated. You can look at them both in blue jeans and *tell* just from the way they look, the way they carry themselves, the way they act, what their personality is. The dress should reflect that."

To achieve the right look for a girl's personality, Kathleen Munson "meticulously develops a theme with her wardrobing." She asks the contestant to complete a personal adjective list that "defines" the image she wants to project to judges. "Let's say you want to be considered intelligent, sophisticated, elegant, and glamorous," says Munson. "You've already *told* me what colors you want. I probably would work with darker colors and straighter lines. If you want to be fun, cute, and darling, I would probably put you in softer colors and softer lines. I might put puffs, ruffles, or bows. There is no question that you can develop a theme or mood with your gown by the line and color."

The most successful gowns perfectly suit the young woman's personal style. "It's got to be something that represents her," explains Richard Guy, who coached six women to the Miss USA throne, "something that she can feel." Your evening gown is a portrait of your personal style. Make it a masterpiece.

80 · Wear the Gown That Makes You Feel Like the Winner

The right gown not only makes the judges feel like they're looking at a winner, it makes the young woman wearing the gown feel like she *is* the winner. "When you find the gown that you absolutely fall in love with, that you know looks great on you," says Kati Fish, co-owner of Arkansas' K.T.'s The Winning Edge, "you automatically walk prouder, with your head held higher and your shoulders back, and you walk more gracefully than you would walk in a dress that was just so-so. Having the right gown makes a big difference when you're competing," says Kati, "because it builds your confidence. You want to make sure that you look your absolute best."

Robin Elliott-Bear, of Robin Elliott Ltd., says: "I tell every girl who is here, 'I want you to feel so good in this gown that if all fifty contestants walked onstage in the same dress, you would still feel like the winner.'"

(BRIDES & BEAUTIES/PHOTO BY DON SEIDMAN)

There's no one "look" that wins, Dana Stephenson,
1993 America's National Teenager, models a feminine,
full-skirted gown style.

Keep in mind that there is no one "right" gown guaranteed to thrill every judge and capture the crown for every girl who wears it. "Everyone has their own opinions," Robin warns, "so when you get into a competition and there are five or seven judges who all have their opinions, you could have a different winner every day of the week. That's why it's important to find a dress that suits the young woman's personality and figure, and that makes her feel the best. Because you cannot make every judge happy." No one can predict what judges will like on a given evening—so wear what makes *you* feel like a winner.

81 · Dare to Be Different

Because what judges will "go for" is unpredictable, many contestants try to improve their odds of winning by copying the gown worn by the reigning queen or a recent titleholder. "Very often people think that a dress is what wins the pageant," observes Elliott-Bear. "They come in knowing all these different gowns the winners have worn. I'll hear, 'Oh yeah, that's Susan Akin's dress,' or 'That's Debra Maffett's dress.' They see it on TV and they think, 'They're winners, they've been there and won, so maybe the same dress will work for me.' They have it in their mind that *this* is the dress that wins."

Unfortunately, copying a previous winner's gown, hoping that it will prove equally lucky for you, is the worst move you could make. Once a gown has been worn by a major winner it is copied relentlessly. Many of your rivals will be copying her "winning look" too. "Every year, whatever Miss America wears, I see *thousands* of those dresses for the next year," Vernon DeSear admits with a chuckle, adding, "Be original!"

Judges tire of seeing so many look-alikes and often will select a young woman wearing a completely different look. Consider Miss USAs Michelle Royer, Shannon Marketic, and Lu Parker. In the midst of the string of winners in strapless gowns, these three women won wearing strikingly different styles—still the right image for Miss USA, but individual. Royer wore a modest, yet elegant, blue gown with long sleeves. Marketic wore a romantic black lace gown with a full skirt and lace shoulder ruffles. Parker wore a plain black gown with a midriff keyhole.

There are other examples of women who dared to be different and won. When the vast majority of Miss Americas had worn white, Carolyn Sapp dared to wear a black velvet-and-lace creation. She won. When most Miss Universes wore light colors, Miss Canada, Karen Baldwin, showed up in a unique black sequin strapless gown with a marabou feather skirt, and won. Sweden's Yvonne Ryding wore an even more unique style—an unfitted, flowing white lace dress and cape, and became Miss Universe 1984. New York's Marie Soden won the 1976 International Rose of Tralee title wearing an unfitted ivory lace caftan. Jamie Solinger won Miss Teen USA in a bright green chiffon dress. Cheryl Prewitt wore a one-of-a-kind floral print chiffon gown with three rhinestone straps across one shoulder. Nothing even remotely like these styles had won before, but the young ladies *made* their gowns winners.

As these titleholders demonstrated, one of the secrets to capturing the crown is wearing an evening gown that is so *beautifully* different that judges can't help but notice you. "Don't be afraid to be different," says Debbie Brown. "I go to so many pageants where you see all these dresses that are the same thing over and over and over. They're just clones. When somebody comes onstage with something different on, you sit up and notice her."

But, unlike winners, who dare to stand out from the crowd, most contestants lack the confidence to be original. Instead, they copy. What they fail to understand is that a true winner does not copy another woman. She has confidence in her own taste and dares to wear what truly flatters her. "A winner

doesn't wear something just because somebody says that's what wins," says Kathleen Munson, author of several modeling videos and books. "She is an individualist who goes with what works for *her*. A winner is not a copy." Dare to be different.

82 · Don't Give Judges an "Excuse" to Mark You Down

It's a tough task to judge a subjective competition where most of the contestants look beautiful. Since judges can't award tens to everybody onstage, scoring usually comes down to a process of elimination. Judges find nitpicky reasons to mark down. Gown mistakes can range from image errors, such as a neckline cut to the navel, to technical errors, such as improper fit and hem length. The secret is to avoid giving the panel any reason to deduct points. As David Bartley put it, "The girl who wins is the one who makes the least mistakes."

Mistakes in the choice of gown eliminate contestants by revealing to judges which girls *don't* have the qualities necessary to be an effective titleholder: good judgment, taste, modesty, or common sense. "I think intelligence plays a part," says Vernon DeSear, who supervised Miss Floridas' wardrobes for national competition. "You have to use your mind and consider what you are portraying about yourself with your gown. If a girl comes out in a dress that is cut down to her navel, that should tell us something about her. What type of girl wants to get up in front of the nation in a dress cut down to here? If the girl does not have a good figure but she wears a skin-tight dress, the judges will wonder, 'Why did she pick this dress?' Two things will come to mind. Either somebody dictated that

"Don't be afraid to be different," advises Debbie Brown, who wardrobed Lu Parker, Miss USA 1994, in an understated gown with a cut-out midriff.

(BRIDES & BEAUTIES/PHOTO BY DON SEIDMAN)

she had to wear this dress because they wanted her to wear it, or she has no idea of what taste is or what looks good on her. So, clothes do come into it."

There is no question that gown gaffes can cost a contestant the crown. Formalwear expert Zola Keller, of South Florida's Zola Keller boutique, recalls a state titleholder whose gown glitches had previously prevented the judges from awarding her the crown. "She was a gorgeous girl, her body was phenomenal, and she spent a fortune on her wardrobe. But it was all wrong! She spent like eight thousand dollars on a Bob Mackie, but it was an 'Elvira' dress—big black sleeves, slit to the navel. It was just *wrong*. It wasn't like she skimped, but she just had no advice." When she lost, the young woman asked the director where she had gone wrong. "The first thing they told her was 'wardrobe'!" She came to Zola for help. "Her problem was that she was 'too much,' so I toned her down—and she won." Don't cost yourself the crown with "image" errors.

One of the most common "technical" mistakes is a gown that fits poorly. The gown should be altered to lay flat against the body, especially around the bodice and waist. There should be no wrinkles or puckers evident as a contestant walks. "You want it to look like it was made just for you," says Annette Gerhart, of Pennsylvania's The Cinderella Shoppe, "not that you just grabbed it off the rack and said, 'Okay, let's go to this pageant and get rolling.' And there are some girls who look like that. As judges, you see some of the most god awful dresses that ever hit a stage—dragging and sagging and lagging behind!"

Another frequent gaffe is a too-short hemline that makes the contestant look like she's outgrown her gown. "It depends on whether the dress is full or straight, but the basic rule is just to let that hem kiss the top of the toe," Gerhart explains. "You don't want it to touch the floor. It's got to be the right length." A "high-water" hemline looks amateurish, while a too-long hemline can trip a young lady onstage. Wear the same shoes at fittings to achieve the right hem length for competition.

When a girl has achieved a winning look, her evening gown's image and technical qualities will blend so smoothly and professionally that judges won't find an excuse to deduct points. "You can look at her onstage, and not see anything that is out of place that takes away from the contestant," explains Robin Elliott-Bear. "You're just going to see a pretty girl in a pretty dress."

At a Glance . . .

Features of a Losing Gown:
- overpowers its wearer
- too-short hem
- poor fit
- plunging neckline or excessive cleavage
- skin-tight gown on an imperfect figure
- slinky beaded gown on a preteen
- clutter: excess ruffles and bows after the teens
- gaudy colors (red and black sequins, rainbow sequins)
- wide hoop skirt when they're out of fashion
- distracting shoes or jewelry

Features of a Winning Gown:
- the right image for the pageant
- right for the girl's personal style
- flattering style for her figure
- flattering color for her hair and skin tones
- neckline that complements her facial shape
- a gorgeous back view
- perfect fit and correct hem length
- beautifully accessorized

Remember, if even one judge reacts negatively to your gown, the points that he/she deducts can mean the difference between your making the top ten or not, or your being the winner—or not. Don't give a judge an excuse to lower your score. Avoid point-losing gown mistakes.

83 · *It's the Look . . . Not the Loot*

The big question: Do you have to wear an expensive gown to win? It depends on the gown and its wearer. Keep in mind, the purpose of a gown is to make the contestant look beautiful, flatter her figure, create a winning image, and convince judges to award her high scores. Any gown that achieves those qualities is a winner. The $500 black velvet strapless number that flatters the young woman's figure and makes her look radiant will score just as highly as its $5,000 black strapless beaded counterpart.

Some programs like Miss America try to limit gown expenses by asking entrants to avoid excessive beading, which is what usually runs up prices. Other programs like America's Junior Miss and Miss Teen of America require simple gowns and encourage borrowing when possible. "We encourage them to borrow the dress they need and minimize the expense when they are involved in participation," asserts Junior Miss director Robert Hedberg. Noting that entrants in many pageants feel the pressure to "keep up" with expensive beaded gowns, Hedberg insists, "That's not our emphasis. It's more on their self-esteem."

Even the high-glamour systems are making an effort to be sensitive to contestants' budgets. Paula Miles, director of six Miss USA/Teen USA state pageants in the South, is pleased to see the recent success of simpler, less-expensive gowns. "I'm so glad to see that. It makes things affordable for all these girls who may not have wealthy parents." One of Paula's queens, Lu Parker, Miss South Carolina-USA, won the 1994 Miss USA title wearing an $1,800 unbeaded black gown—cheap as national-level gowns go.

As these winners prove, it's the look—not the loot—that counts:

- Miss America 1994—won in a $395 Lycra gown
- Miss America 1993—crowned in a borrowed strapless gown
- Miss Teen-USA 1993—won in a $37 gown
- Miss America 1988—won in a donated bridal gown she altered
- Miss Florida 1987—won in a $300 gown
- First runner-up to Miss America 1980—paid $9 for a gown at Goodwill; seamstresses added beading
- Miss America 1977—one of her competition gowns cost $29, the other was bought on sale at a department store
- Miss America 1976—her gown retailed for $250
- Miss USA 1973—won wearing a borrowed gown

That is not to say that winners haven't won wearing expensive gowns. For many years, girls from states which could afford lavish wardrobes or had generous gown donors dominated the major pageants. Better training of national judges has improved judging by teaching panelists to judge the *girl*, not the gown. Eliminating group judging, where contestants lined up side by side for comparison judging, has also improved the dynamics of evening-gown judging.

There are alternatives to purchasing costly gowns. Many contestants now rent gowns or purchase former contestants' gowns and alter them. Borrowing is another option. Maya Walker, first runner-up to Miss America 1989, told me that she brought several borrowed formal dresses. Shawn Weatherly, Miss South Carolina-USA, won the 1980 Miss USA and Miss Universe titles wearing a $10,000 gown on loan from famed designer Stephen Yearick, according to her state director.

It's also possible to have a gown made by a seamstress or family member. The public rarely hears about the contestants who won major titles wearing homemade gowns. Elizabeth Ward won the 1982 Miss America Pageant in a dress her grand-mother had sewn from a lace tablecloth and punched with rhinestones. Mona Grudt won the 1990 Miss Universe title wearing a simple, white satin strapless gown a friend made. She placed first in evening gown, beating a custom-made, fully beaded gown by celebrity designer Bob Mackie. As such cases demonstrate, qualified judges do not view a candidate's pretty, correctly tailored, homemade gown as a liability if she is oth-erwise an outstanding candidate for the crown. Evelyn Ay, a former Miss America and respected state and national judge, told me that her reaction to a superb contestant wearing a home-sewn gown is often, "I know that's a homemade dress, but boy, look what she can *do* with that homemade dress!" Keep in mind that when judges are scoring local or state contestants, they understand that the pageant committee will rewardrobe the eventual winner for the next level of competition. If the panel is convinced that a young woman is the most qualified candidate for the title, she could be wearing a potato sack and win. Judges are not going to lose their best girl on a techni-cality.

Additionally, good judges do *not* consider the probable value of the gown when scoring. What they will consider (or *should* consider) is whether the gown complements the girl, and if it brings out her beauty and contributes to a lovely overall pic-ture. "If a girl is really secure in who she is, whether she's in a hundred-fifty-dollar gown or a fifteen-thousand-dollar gown, she's going to be beautiful," asserts national judge Sam Haskell. "How much she spends on her gown doesn't matter to me. If it works, I'm going to point it."

In evening gown a contestant should focus on looking her most beautiful—regardless of price. "Kim Aiken's dress was three hundred ninety-five dollars, which goes to show you that it isn't cost," says Debbie Brown. "A lot of girls think that they've got to buy a three thousand dollar designer gown to win. You don't have to do that. You need to wear what looks good on *you*. If it is a three-hundred-fifty-dollar gown, but it looks great on you, then do it. If the two-thousand-dollar dress looks good on you, then do that one. Wear what looks best on *you*."

The goal is not to spend a king's ransom on an evening gown—but to look like a queen.

THE ART OF THE EVENING GOWN

In addition to considering what type of gown best reflects her personality and creates a winning image, a contestant must also evaluate what styles, fabrics, and colors are most flattering to her figure shape, height, hair color and style, and skin tones under stark stage lights. The objective isn't to find the most eye-catching gown but the gown that makes the young woman look her most beautiful.

84 · Flatter Your Figure With "Figure Camouflage"

In an era when the typical student spends most of her young lifetime in jeans and T-shirts or work-out clothes, a contestant may have no idea what gown styles look good on her. "A lot of times when they come in they have never been in a pageant and they've never even worn a gown, so we try on," says Zola Keller, who has outfitted numerous state and national winners, including Leanza Cornett. "She needs to see, 'Okay, this bottom looks good on me, but this top doesn't.' If it's the first time she's ever put on a gown, she won't have any idea what she is supposed to look like." The only way to find that ideal gown, says Zola, is, "Try on a hundred different gowns—gowns with sleeves, without sleeves, halters, strapless. You've got to try on."

Thanks to recent changes in evening gown guidelines to discourage cookie-cutter beaded gowns and encourage simplicity, entrants can successfully wear a wider range of styles in competition. "I think pageants are becoming a little more open-minded now," says Debbie Brown. "I love it because now, if you look good in a beaded gown, you can wear a beaded gown. If you have big hips and you look better in a chiffon skirt, then wear a chiffon skirt. You're not going to score lower. It's okay to wear what looks good on you."

First, to pick the perfect gown a young lady must know her figure type. Once she understands her figure's assets and flaws she can use "figure camouflage" to emphasize her best features, hide her flaws, and balance her body proportions. Such "camouflage" is accomplished by combining line, color, detail, and fabric to create the right *visual illusions*. It's all sleight-of-eye. "Clothing is nothing more than playing games with people's eyes," explains formalwear specialist Annette Gerhart. "It's drawing the eye where you want it to go." The simple secret to figure camouflage is, "De-accentuate the negative and accentuate the positive." (See Tip #85, "Guide to Figure Camouflage.")

Know Your "Tools"

Line: The first rule of figure camouflage is to use a gown's lines to "correct" figure flaws. "Draw your eyes to the areas you want to accentuate," advises Kati Fish. "The lines of a gown can do a lot to conceal large hips or thick thighs, or even give the illusion that someone is taller or shorter than they actually are." The eye follows the lines of an evening gown. Horizontal lines draw the eye sideways to shorten and widen. Vertical lines draw the eye up and down to lengthen and slenderize. Diagonal and curved lines soften and add curves depending upon their placement. Try on many styles to see how different lines make your figure look.

Fabric: Fabric is another tool for figure camouflage. If you have figure flaws, avoid clingy fabrics or second-skin beaded looks that emphasize problem areas like a tummy, saddlebags, or fleshy hips. "They can't have any bulges or bumps on their body if they're going to wear that kind of fabric," explains designer Tricia Copelin, "because it molds to them." Fabrics like velvet, satin, brocades, heavy laces, chiffon, and tulle provide the best camouflage.

Detail: Detailing is a visual magnet. Use eye-catching detailing to draw judges' attention onto pretty features and away from figure flaws. "You are playing games with where you want to draw their eyes," says Annette. "If there is a lot of interest around the neckline, the eye is going to be drawn to the neckline. If the interest is on the sleeve, the eye will be drawn to the sleeve. If there is nothing," she says, chuckling, "It's, 'Here's my bod!'" Direct judges' eyes where you want them to go with pretty detailing such as rhinestone or beaded artwork, lace ruffles, or fur trim.

Color: Colors can create optical illusions that make a figure look heavier or lighter, wider or thinner. Use correct color choices to reshape a figure and balance body proportions. Dark colors recede and slenderize the body, especially when carried from neck to toe. Black defines the shape it covers. White, lights, and brights advance and slightly enlarge the body. Bold colors call attention to the area they cover. Muted shades of the same colors are more slenderizing.

Although the right lines, colors, detailing, and fabrics can greatly improve a figure's appearance onstage, contestants often discover that their most flattering look involves a combination of qualities they've never considered before. Be open-minded and experiment.

85 · Guide to Figure Camouflage

As you shop for your perfect evening gown, take along this guide to figure camouflage for style ideas:

The Basics at a Glance

- Use detailing to draw attention where you want it (and thus away from problem areas).
- The eye follows the "lines" of the gown.
- Horizontal lines shorten and widen.
- Vertical lines add height and slenderize.
- Diagonal and curved lines soften and add curves.
- Light and bold colors advance and enlarge areas.
- Bright colors make a figure look larger while muted shades of the same color are more slenderizing.
- Dark colors define the shape they cover.
- Dark colors recede and slenderize the body if carried from neck to toe.
- A monochromatic color theme (neck to toes) lengthens.
- Contrasting solids cut body length, shorten the body.

Find Your Figure

Too Short:
- Create one long, unbroken vertical line to look taller.
- Draw eye upward with detailing at neck or bust.
- Have all lines and seams going vertically.
- Create a long, narrow rectangular silhouette.
- Don't "cut" the body with belts, waistlines, peplums.
- Avoid contrasting solids, hip sashes, full skirts.

• Best bets are fitted beaded gowns and straight strapless gowns with an Empire waistline or no waistline.

Heavy Hips and Thighs:
• Balance body by concealing hips and widening shoulders.
• Draw eyes up off lower body with bodice detailing, off-the-shoulder ruffles, puff sleeves, fur trim across shoulders.
• Flowing, tailored, or flared skirts are best.
• Peplums and tulip overskirts can help conceal.
• Proportion shoulders/sleeves to width of the hips.
• Avoid second-skin fabrics, liquid beading, halters.
• Best bet is black velvet with an eye-catching bodice.
• Try a vermicelli-beaded gown in rich color with padded shoulders and Basque waist.
• Pretty upper body? Try an Empire-waisted strapless (or spaghetti straps) in a flowing fabric.

Too Thin:
• Choose white, bright, or neon colors, or metallics.
• Draped styles, graceful flowing fabrics are ideal.
• Billowing sleeves conceal thin arms.
• Try a fitted waist, flowing skirt, full sleeves.
• Avoid fitted strapless gowns in dark colors.

Thick-Waisted:
• Straight gowns look best.
• Don't emphasize the waist. Avoid belts.
• Long-line bras and bust-to-hip bustiers trim waist.
• Strapless fitted gowns with stays mold a waistline.
• Diagonal starburst beading slenderizes waist.
• Try a straight gown with one diagonal shoulder strap.
• Try Empire- or Basque-waisted styles, or a strapless gown with Empire waist and flowing skirt.

Short-Waisted:
• Avoid wide waistbands and belts.
• Avoid color changes at waist; wrap or diagonal bodices.
• Try a dropped waist, Empire waist, or hip-sashed gown.
• Straight gown lines can lengthen the torso.

Long-Waisted:
• No dropped waistlines or hip-sashed gowns.
• Try a wide waistband or obi sash up to ribs.
• An Empire waist with flowing skirt conceals below the ribcage.

Small-Busted:
• Wear almost any style by padding the bustline.
• Draped, wrapped, or heavily beaded bodices add fullness.
• Wear a gown with sewn-in bust cups.
• Conceal bust with shoulder ruffle, fur band across bust, or an elegant bow bodice.

Large-Busted:
• A big bust is fashionable: Don't conceal, tone down.
• V-necklines (not too deep) and wide sweetheart necklines are flattering.
• Show off bust in a fitted strapless gown.
• Try a beaded gown with a Basque waistline.
• Wide skirt base, flared hems balance a large bust.

Narrow Shoulders:
• To broaden, draw the eye to outer shoulders.
• Padded shoulders and puffed or gathered sleeves widen shoulders.
• Best bet is a widely scooped neckline or extra-wide "sweetheart" neckline and padded shoulders.
• Lace ruffles, fur shoulder trim help conceal shoulders.
• Try a strapless gown with long hair covering shoulders.
• Avoid halters or any top with lines "aimed" at neck.

Wide Shoulders:
- Draw the eye inward toward the neck and face.
- Try halters, turtlenecks, and stand-up beaded collars.
- Avoid padded shoulders.
- Try sheer lace sleeves, beaded bodice, flowing skirt.
- Balance shoulders with a flared "mermaid" hem.
- Widen hips with a peplum or tulip skirt for balance.
- Broad shoulders are fashionable. Try showing them off.

Short Neck:
- Try a deep-V neckline or sweetheart neckline.
- No high-neck gowns or stand-up collars (especially worn with padded shoulders—you'll "lose" your neck).
- Avoid heavy shoulder padding (it cuts neck length).
- Try strapless/spaghetti-strap gown styles. (Compare strapless gowns with medium hair worn down with curls dusting shoulders, then with hair worn up.)

Thin Neck/Protruding Collarbones:
- Try high collars, beaded collars, or a soft ruffle.
- Cover area with chiffon sash, drape ends down back.
- Avoid strapless gowns, revealing necklines.
- However, if it's a long pretty neck, show it off.

Whatever the figure flaw, recommended gown style, or contestant's personality and age—a winning evening gown will always draw the judges' attention to the young woman's face. "The most important thing is to enhance and bring out her *face*," asserts noted designer Beverly McGinn. Because, a *person* wins the crown. Not a body.

86 · Test Colors Under Mock Stage Lighting

Just as the right gown design can improve a figure, color can help a contestant achieve a winning look.

One of the factors a contestant should keep in mind is how

her gown color will look under stage lights. "It's amazing the difference stage lighting makes on a gown," says Kati Fish. "Because of the fabrics gowns are made from today, rich crepe silks and chiffons, the difference between regular lighting and stage flood lighting is like night and day. It can almost make them look like two different gowns."

Intense stage lighting can not only alter how gown colors look onstage, it can change how those colors affect a contestant's skin tones and hair color. "Stage lighting can actually change the way a color looks on your skin," Kati explains. Under stage lights the wrong colors can be unflattering: turning dyed-blond hair brassy, casting yellow, green, or grayish tints onto the face, or draining color from a fair complexion. "Your lighting and choice of color are important," says pageant consultant Kathleen Munson. "They can kill as well as enhance. On warm-toned skin, pinks can be really bad. If you've got very cool tones, peaches can look bad. Anything with a bit of green or yellow will take on that quality onstage, which very few skin tones can survive." Clearly, the appearance of a fabric color under stage lights can greatly affect how a young woman looks—and scores—in the evening gown competition.

To help contestants evaluate possible gown colors, experts recommend testing gowns under mock stage lights to see how each color will appear onstage. As mentioned earlier, many pageant shops now offer state-of-the-art "lighting rooms" equipped with lighting systems to test wardrobing. "It's really important that you know what that color is going to look like when you get onstage," says Fish. "You want to know exactly how you are going to be perceived by the judges."

Even film stars go to great lengths to ensure that their formalwear is flattering onstage. According to *Parade* magazine, for her appearance at a recent Academy awards ceremony, Barbra Streisand tested the same gown in different colors on-camera before deciding on her attire. (After testing black, white, and dusty rose, she opted for the rose.) As Streisand's painstaking efforts demonstrate, image-conscious women find their most flattering colors before they step onstage in front of millions of armchair critics. To look your very best in competition, pretest your gown's fabric color under stage lighting.

87 · Find Your Best Gown Colors

An evening gown should enhance a young woman's beauty by complementing her unique skin tones and hair coloring. Unfortunately, even without the complications of stage lighting, colors can be unpredictable, affecting complexions and hair colors in surprising ways. "Colors either cast a yellow shade or a pink shade onto the face," explains pageant clothing designer Beverly McGinn. "If you've got a yellow-based shade, it's going to yellow your makeup instead of keeping you nice and bright. Some colors can make [contestants] look very sallow. Other colors will cast a green shade onto their face. The color goes right back onto the face. So we color-code." Color analysis enables a contestant's wardrobers to understand the skin tones they are dealing with. Knowing that the girl's complexion has golden or blue undertones, or is ruddy or sallow, helps in the selection of colors and shades that are most flattering.

Keep in mind that colors come in an entire range of shades, each of which will "behave" differently on an individual. Take reds. One shade of red, perhaps an orange-red, could look awful on a contestant, while a wine red might make her look radiant. According to experts, any girl can wear any color, but the shade of that color must be correct for her hair and skin tones. "I have found over the years that there isn't a woman who cannot wear all colors," observes Annette Gerhart. "It depends on the *shade* of that color and on her makeup. Of course, there are certain shades that will be more becoming, but find the right tone and you can wear *any* color." That right shade will bring a healthy glow to the face, minimize shadows, make eyes and teeth appear bright, and flatter the hair coloring.

Although hair color—both the girl's natural shade and any dyes or highlights—helps determine the most flattering gown colors, don't limit your early choices with preconceived ideas about what colors you're "supposed" to wear. "I don't think any hair color is limited," asserts Kathleen Munson, who has written several books on modeling. "I think you need to explore the possibilities and find what's best for you."

What They Wore

The following is a list of the evening gown colors worn by major pageant winners, according to their hair color:

Blondes: White, black, pink, coral pink, mint green, baby blue, yellow, aqua/turquoise, red, beige, royal blue, and gold tones.

Brunettes: White, ivory, turquoise, pastel aqua, pink, peach, black, lilac, yellow, red, medium blues, beige/skin tone, magenta, bright green, gold lamé, silver, floral print, and rainbow chiffon.

Women of Color: White, red, black, turquoise, gold lamé, lilac, ice blue, peach, gold beading, silver beading.

Redheads/Auburn: White, Kelly to hunter greens, medium pastel aqua, turquoise, and black.

To determine *your* best evening gown colors, be creative. Consider (but don't be held captive by) the results of color analysis, and experiment with dozens of colors, from those that already command your closet to those you've never tried before. Your evening gown is your portrait. Color yourself beautiful.

88 · Use "Color Psychology" to Convey Image

Understand the psychology of color. "Sixty percent of a person's reaction to any situation is based on color," claims Carlton Wagner, director of the Wagner Institute for Color Research.[1] A contestant can use colors to control how judges react to her during the evening gown competition.

Every color has a distinct image that sends a message about the wearer. Although that message is silent, it is so predictable that television and film wardrobe specialists use wardrobe colors to silently telegraph an actress's character to viewers. "If the actress is playing a virginal scene of honesty I am certainly not going to have her in red," explained "Dallas" costumer Bill Travell during a *Miami Herald* interview. "I'll put her in a clear, lovely color to create an aura of honesty, like shell pink. And if you know she is telling a lie, I can help her in her dialogue by putting her in an olive green or another shady, muddy, untrusting color."

Likewise, colors craft very specific images in pageants. "For instance," says Kathleen Munson, "I think it's a very different contestant who comes out in a black gown than comes out in a white gown. Black develops an image of sophistication, glamour, maturity, and elegance onstage. Light colors will be more whimsical and younger, and red is reactionary." White creates an even more distinct image, according to designer Ada Duckett. "White represents purity. Queen Elizabeth wore white for her coronation and brides wear white because they are special. The same way, most Miss Americas have worn white."

From the standpoint of human response, a gown's color subtly conveys a specific image to judges. For instance, the candidate in glow-in-the-dark orange fabric will project a far different image than the young lady in dainty pastel pink. Since color and style define a young woman's image and tell judges who she is, contestants should choose gown colors with great care.

Different colors can be consciously chosen to reflect a girl's personality, to soften an overpowering personality, or to "create" a specific image.

If Colors Could Speak

Research has demonstrated that colors have definite "personalities"[2,3,4,5]:

- WHITE—pure, clean, innocent, ladylike, uniforms
- IVORY—elegant, refined, feminine, classic
- RED—confident, aggressive, exciting, outgoing, sexy
- PINK—feminine, nonthreatening, delicate, adolescent
- BLUES—calm, conservative, dignified, #1 favorite color
- NAVY—conservative, reserved, traditional, official
- AQUA—outgoing; men find it extremely attractive on women
- YELLOW—cheerful, friendly, outgoing, "people person"
- ORANGE—active, cheerful, enthusiastic, stimulating
- GREEN—open, refreshing, outdoorsy, restful, not in good health—hospital green
- DARK GREEN—refined, associated with money, drab
- BROWN—reliable, friendly, practical, dull, drab
- GRAY—conservative, classic, refined, calm, stodgy
- PURPLE—dignified, associated with royalty, sadness
- WINE/BURGUNDY—regal, understated elegance, wealth
- BLACK—sophisticated, serious, mature, dignified
- PASTELS—soothing, youthful, feminine, nonthreatening

While color can be used to develop a specific image, color alone won't complete that look. Color must be combined with the right *style* to create an exact image. For instance, a red velvet strapless gown creates a very different image than a red sequin gown with a plunging neckline. A red chiffon gown with a flowing skirt and lace bodice creates still another image. The same chiffon gown in white changes the image more. By carefully combining styles and colors, a contestant can develop an exact image that makes her look and feel like a winner.

Use color psychology to create a specific image that "tells" judges who you are. "You really have to understand what's best for you," says Munson. "Dorothy Benham won in red [sequins]. Susan Perkins won in a purple [chiffon] gown. You've got to go with what works for *you*." Make sure the color you choose sends the right message.

89 · Know the Winning Colors

According to my statistical research, there are specific gown colors that are consistently successful in national and international pageants. The fact that certain colors fare better than others does *not* mean that the color wins the title for a girl. It means that in competitive situations judges have consistently responded well to young women wearing those colors.

Frankly, judges don't care about the shade of a contestant's gown. We are talking about *gut reactions* in fast-paced judging situations. A judge simply may not react as favorably to a young woman in, let's say, an olive-green gown as he or she might to a contestant in white. In respect to instant reactions, all colors are not equal.

The Winning Colors

Here, in order of overall success, are the gown colors that make the semi-finals, the finals, or win the crown in major pageants, with consistency over time:

Miss America	*Miss USA*	*Miss Universe*
White	White	White
Black	Black	Red
Pink	Mid/royal blues	Black

Miss America	Miss USA	Miss Universe
Bold turquoise	Pink	Mid/royal blues
Lilac	Red	Silver metallic
Red	Pastel blues	Pink
Pastel aqua	Skin tone/beiges	Gold metallic
Mid-blues	Yellow	Bold turquoise
Skin tone/beiges	Gold metallic	Ivory/cream
Yellows	Bold turquoise	Lilac
Silver	Peach	Greens
Peach	Ivory/cream	Light blues
Prints/designs	Deeper blues	Multicolor bead
Light blues		Peach

Keep in mind that the success rate of some colors fluctuates from year to year as contestants copy what won the year before or are influenced by fashion trends. For instance, a decade ago, black—currently a highly successful color—wouldn't even have made the list for Miss America. Yet, white has unquestionably remained the most successful gown color in all major pageants over many decades.

What colors don't win? The biggest losers in evening gown competition are brown, gray, camel, rust, mustard, olive green, navy blue, dark purple, orange, and stripes.

These color patterns apply specifically to national- and international-level competition. A far wider range of colors win on the local, state, and regional levels, which means that the lower the level of competition, the more colors you can successfully wear.

Recent Trends in Gown Colors

Want to know who wore what winning colors? The following is a listing of recent major pageant titleholders and the evening gown colors they wore to win their coveted crowns.*

*Some winners are listed twice: Miss USAs who changed gowns for the Miss Universe Pageant, and Miss Americas who wore different gowns for the preliminary and final evening gown competitions.

Winners in White:

Miss America 1995	Miss USA 1993
Miss World 1994	Mrs. America 1992
Miss Junior Miss 1994	Miss USSR 1990
Miss Universe 1993	Miss Universe 1990
Mrs. America 1993	Miss T.E.E.N. 1990

Winners in Pastels:

Miss World-America 1993—pink
Miss USA 1986—coral pink
Miss America 1985—pastel aqua
Miss USA 1985—pink
Miss America 1984—lilac
Miss Universe 1981—pink

Winners in Bold Colors:

Miss America 1993—yellow
Miss Teen USA 1993—magenta
Miss 1992 World-America—red
Miss Universe 1992—red
Miss T.E.E.N. 1992—green
Miss Teen USA 1992—green
Miss Universe 1991—red
Miss America 1991—hot aqua
Miss USA 1991—red
Miss Universe 1986—hot aqua

Winners in Black:

Miss America 1994
Miss USA 1994
Miss America 1992

Miss USA 1992
Mrs. United States 1992
Miss USA 1990
Miss USSR 1989

Winners in Metallic Gold or Silver:
Miss Universe 1994
first runner-up, Miss Universe 1994
Mrs. USA 1993
Miss Universe 1977

The perfect evening gown will combine the best color and style for the contestant's hair color, skin tones, and complexion, make her look her prettiest under harsh stage lights, fit flawlessly, and convey the image of a winner to judges. The right gown can make the difference between winning and losing, so don't settle for just a pretty gown. Aim for perfection.

THE FINISHING TOUCHES

In much the same way that a quality frame finishes and complements a masterpiece, the right final touches—undergarments, jewelry, and shoes—complete a contestant's look to create a polished winning picture.

90 · Flatter Your Figure With the Right "Foundation"

Proper undergarments are the "foundation" for that winning look. "Just like a house, the proper foundation is the most important thing," asserts Robin Elliott-Bear. Pageant undergarments include backless long-line bras, bust-to-hip bustiers, bust cups, waist cinchers, T-panties, and hosiery with built-in panties.

With the bust being an important feature in pageant clothing, the right brassiere is important. A good bra shapes, defines, supports, or builds up the breasts. Many contestants wear long-line bras or bust-to-hip bustiers, which provide support and create a sleek line, especially with strapless gowns. Yet, with second-skin fabrics they may not work. "If you have a real clingy fabric like a Lycra or matte jersey, you can't use either one of those because the lines will show," Tricia Copelin explains. Also, on some girls any extra flesh on the hips can bulge out where the garment ends. To simplify dressing, many designers sew brassiere cups or bustiers right into the gown.

New competitors often wonder what type of panties to wear. Although some girls wear "T-panties," pageant clothing specialists usually recommend creating a smooth waist-to-thigh silhouette with sheer-to-waist pantyhose. "Don't wear panties," advises Copelin. "I usually suggest that they wear pantyhose with a cotton panty so they don't have a panty line. You can tell a panty-line in almost any straight dress, whether it's fully beaded or jersey, so I tell them to wear Underalls. If you have a poochy tummy, wear control-top hose or even sheer-support hose." Slips are seldom worn today since most gowns are lined for modesty.

Since undergarments shape the body beneath the gown, they must be worn during fittings to ensure proper fit later in competition.

91 · Add the Winning Touches

While lingerie creates a quality foundation for a contestant's evening gown, the right jewelry and shoes add the winning touches that complete her look.

Jewelry Fit for a Queen

As the accessory closest to a contestant's face, her jewelry must be impeccable. "Accessories are the frame to the picture," says Thomas Tolbert. "Jewelry enhances and finishes the look. If it overpowers you and you look at the jewelry before you look at her face, then it's wrong. You've got to consider the neckline, the girl's weight, her hair, and her eyes. There are a lot of things to be considered."

The dress design, facial shape and size and hairstyle are the most important factors in selecting earrings to complement a total look. "I don't so much look at her face as I look at her overall appearance from the head to bust area," says Kati Fish. "If she has a long neck and she is wearing a strapless dress, she can wear a really long earring. If she is wearing a dress that comes up high around her neck or close to the neck, you don't want to have long earrings. You'll want more of a button style. If a girl has a small face and she's wearing a flowing gown, I'll get a more dainty earring, as opposed to someone who is going with a completely beaded look with very full hair."

Contestants often make mistakes in their choice of earrings. "They should be in good taste and the right size," says Zola Keller. "Medium, not these massive things covering up the whole ear, and not those 'dusters' hanging down to their shoulders. If the earrings are too big and gaudy, that's the first thing the judge is going to see. They're not going to pay any attention to what she is wearing below that, because the earrings got the first attention. When I get a girl ready, I don't want one thing to be picked out: 'Her earrings are too long' or 'Her earrings are too big.' I don't want the judge to even *notice* them. I want the judges to look at the girl overall."

Formal hair accessories like an elegant crystal barrette can be an attractive accessory with a simple gown, such as a black velvet strapless gown. However, other items of jewelry, such as necklaces, bracelets, rings, watches, and ankle bracelets, shouldn't be worn because they clutter the picture. Avoid anything that pulls judges' attention off your face.

Sensational Shoes

The right shoes also help finish the picture the contestant is creating. Competitors in their teens and up should always wear high heels in the evening gown competition to create a taller, slimmer, more elegant body line. Pageant shoes are available with heels ranging from one to four inches. Although most contestants wear traditional three- to three-and-a-half-inch heels, petite girls sometimes opt for four-inch heels to add height, and pre- to early-teen contestants wear flats or short heels. As a rule, the taller the shoe heel, the sexier the look, and the more difficult it is to walk properly. When unsure of the proper heel height, ask the pageant director for recommendations.

Pageant apparel specialists differ on their specific style recommendations. Some experts prefer clear open-toe shoes with rhinestone trim, while others prefer an elegant fabric or mesh evening pump. Whatever the choice, a competition shoe should always feature a low-cut "throat." The higher the front cut of the shoe, the clunkier it looks.

(C. P. ANNIE PRODUCTIONS, INC.)

The right shoes add the winning touch to an evening gown.

The advantage of a clear shoe is its "invisibility" onstage. "I prefer the acrylic shoes with rhinestones for evening gown because it's softer," says Robin Elliott-Bear. "Nobody's looking at your feet—and that's the point with acrylic shoes. The judges are below you when you are competing so you don't want your foot to be the first thing they see. The acrylic shoe doesn't jump out at them." Yet, she prefers a matching pump with black gowns. "When the dress is so dark, if you wear the acrylic shoe, it's such a contrast." Courtney Gibbs became Miss USA 1988 wearing sleek black pumps with her beaded black strapless gown.

Other wardrobe specialists prefer traditional closed pumps over transparent open-toe shoes. "I've never liked the clear shoes, because when you stand there your toes are hanging out," says Annette Gerhart. "Why would you want to wear a drop-dead gorgeous evening gown with your toes hanging out? I think a closed pump is always the safest bet. It's a very safe, comfortable, neutral shoe and it completes the look." With a traditional evening pump, consider the gown and the total look. "It all depends on your gown," says Kati Fish. "If you've got a dress without beading, you probably won't want a shoe with a lot of sparkle because you don't want your feet to take away from the dress. You'll probably want to go with satin and peau de soie shoes that can be dyed to match the dress." Miss Universes Porntip Nakhirunkanok ('88) and Dayanara Torres ('93), and Miss Teen of America 1994, Carla McPherson, wore simple white pumps to complement their white gowns."

Another choice is a delicate, open-toe, sling-back formal shoe in the gown's color, as worn by Miss Americas Dorothy Benham, Kylene Barker, Susan Powell, and Vanessa Williams. However, warns Gerhart, "Sling-backs can get caught in hemlines. I can't tell you how many girls have come in with hems ripped out from the buckle catching."

A beaded shoe may be acceptable with a lavishly beaded

gown, but only if the shoe matches perfectly and does not over-power the dress. "If a girl is dripping in bugle beads, then she can carry that right down into a beaded shoe," advises Annette, "but you've got to watch the all-sequin pump because it can make your feet look fat." Metallic silver or gold shoes usually call too much attention to the feet onstage. Even so, Deborah Carthy-Due won the 1985 Miss Universe title wearing shiny gold shoes with an ankle-length white beaded slip-dress accent-ed with gold beading. (Hey, a winner *makes* the rules!)

The stunning "Starburst" evening slipper with a sheer mesh toe trimmed with rhinestones is recommended by Thomas Tol-bert because of the style's ability to keep attention off the feet. "Your eye goes down to the rhinestones, and once it hits the toes, for some reason, the eye goes right back up, so again you're looking at her face—not the feet. It's an elegant shoe that shows the foot off very well—and it's comfortable."

Comfort is crucial since the fit of a shoe directly affects how a young woman walks while onstage. When a girl's shoes fit poorly, they hurt her feet, and her walk is stilted. When you find your ideal evening pumps break them in, advises Cheryl Prewitt-Salem, of C.P. Annie Productions footwear, "because when a girl wears shoes onstage that she doesn't normally wear, her feet are killing her—and that should never be. You should be comfortable onstage."

The bottom line with any accessory, from shoes to bras, is get used to them before competition, because discomfort is a dead giveaway. "Don't wear new shoes, period," advises Kenn Berry, a Miss New York regional field director and veteran judge. "When you walk out onstage, any judge worth his salt can tell in a minute. If you're going to buy new shoes for a pageant, get them four months before and walk in them, work in them, do your housework in them. The same with undergarments for the evening gown competition. Don't just buy a new undergarment and come out onstage in it. If you're not used to it, it's going to show. You have to be perfectly relaxed in what you wear. Otherwise you look as if you're uneasy—and those judges *can* tell."

EIGHT

Winning Onstage Communication:

The Art of Interviews, Statements, and Final Questions

These girls have to be able to SPEAK.
RICHARD GUY, GUYREX ASSOCIATES

Onstage communication is one of the most important aspects of pageant competition for it has a great effect on the judges and often determines who wears the crown.

The purpose of onstage communication segments is to test each contestant's ability to think on her feet and express herself under pressure, which reveals to judges how she would handle the interviews and speeches required of a titleholder. The eventual winner must be able to converse with reporters, give press conferences, deliver speeches with little preparation, and converse comfortably on live television during her reign. Major national titleholders often glide off the runway and onto the sets of *Larry King Live, Late Show With David Letterman,* and a slew of morning talk shows. There simply isn't time to teach the winner to communicate in public. Therefore, judges place a great emphasis on a contestant's ability to sound like a winner in the spotlight.

Onstage communication also reveals which contestants have the outgoing personality to chat cordially and confidently with everyone from Bob Hope during a television special to an executive at a sponsor's reception. "The Miss USA system is looking for a *hostess*," says Kati Fish, Miss Arkansas-USA 1993, "someone who will be able to stand in a cocktail party, mingle, and carry on a conversation with anyone. By the time you get to the national level you've got to be a natural. You've got to be able to speak easily on just about any subject—whether you are talking to one person, five thousand, or five million."

What Judges Look For

While the judging criteria will differ from pageant to pageant, some of the qualities judges consider include:

- personality, charm, sincerity, charisma
- confidence, poise, and composure before an audience
- intelligence
- pleasant conversationalist
- ability to think on one's feet under pressure
- able to articulate one's opinions and values
- voice, vocabulary, grammar, eloquence
- content of remarks
- courage of her convictions
- use of wit and humor
- suitability as a role model/sponsor spokesperson
- overall impression

Onstage Communication Formats Differ

Pageants use several different formats to test contestants' onstage communication skills:

- a brief introductory statement
- a memorized speech on a theme
- a "commercial" for her state or country
- an informal conversation with the emcee

- a judge's question to a contestant
- final questions (often identical, with an isolation booth)

Most pageants ask entrants to introduce themselves with a brief prepared statement mentioning their city, state, college, major, career goals, and possibly a sponsor. Remarks can be witty or formal, or share a philosophy of life, favorite quotation, or unusual hobby.

Pageants may also conduct onstage interviews. The Miss USA, Miss Teen USA, and Miss Universe contests place heavy emphasis on speaking skills with three onstage interviews: the semi-finalists' conversation with the host, the top six's questions from judges, and the finalists' identical final questions with use of an isolation booth.

Finalists' interviews are another popular format. In Mrs. America, the five finalists answer questions from the judges. In Miss America, the top five are seated onstage where they chat informally with the host and then explain the social issues "platform" each would address if selected the winner. Their scores count as "bonus" points. Likewise, America's Junior Miss, a "junior Miss America Pageant," recently adopted top five conversations with the emcee.

Other pageants ask entrants to deliver a personal statement, brief speech, or "commercial." GuyRex's Miss United States Pageant (formerly Miss World-America) includes a "verbal expression" segment, an informal conversation with the emcee, followed by a memorized "commercial" on a given theme, usually a sales pitch for her state or nation. In the America's Junior Miss Pageant's "presence and composure" segment, "contestants are asked to speak publicly to the audience, to make a value statement of some type," says official Robert Hedberg. "It can take many different formats, including a question or comment concerning a relevant subject."

Whatever the format, the quality sought is always the

same—effective, pleasant, diplomatic communication skills under pressure. The bottom line, says Richard Guy, is "These girls have got to be able to *speak!*"

Tips:
- Always take a breath before speaking.
- Don't grab the microphone from the emcee.
- Don't lean toward a hand-held or stand microphone.
- Even if you are scared—look confident and relaxed.
- Jitters can raise the voice. Lower your voice a bit.
- If the host asks you a question, don't stare at the judges when answering. Look at the host, then include the audience and judges as you speak.
- If a judge asks you a question, smile at him or her first, then include the other judges and audience.
- Get to the point. Don't ramble.

92 · Use Communication to Create a Winning Image

Onstage communication segments provide an ideal opportunity for a contestant to create a winning image. Introductory statements, casual conversations, and final questions all help judges to get to know the candidates better. Every time a young woman opens her mouth to speak, her personal "style" is immediately evident. Is she a casual collegiate athlete, an intellectual law student, a wholesome future kindergarten teacher, or a gorgeous, but ditzy, aspiring actress? The way she communicates "types" the young woman.

Of course, whether the format is an interview or brief speech, creating a winning image depends upon using carefully chosen personal information to "mold" how judges view you. For instance, the success of an onstage interview depends on the quality of the material the emcee has to draw upon. "We take the information off of their fact sheet and entry form and they have a conversation based on that information," explains

Tina Birkett, of the Miss Teen All American Pageant. If a contestant's entry form or fact sheet offers interesting hobbies, athletic awards, academic pursuits, career goals, or family trivia, the emcee will have an assortment of colorful topics to ask her about. The better the topics, the better the questions, the better the onstage interview, the better your scores. (See Tip #3, "Use Your Entry Form to Create a Winning Image.")

If the onstage communication segment requires a brief personal statement, take that opportunity to emphasize what is most impressive about yourself. Consider the brief introductory remarks offered by Kaye Lani Rae Rafko, Miss Michigan 1987, an oncology-hematology nurse who worked with terminal cancer and AIDS patients. Kaye Lani's life's dream was to open a hospice in her community and she wisely focused on the special profession she had dedicated her life to:

"I am a twenty-four-year-old registered nurse working in the specialized area of oncology-hematology. I will further my education to obtain a master's degree and continue my work with the terminally ill."[1]

Simple, powerful, and perfectly descriptive of the woman the judges chose to honor with the national title.

Another effective strategy is to use family adages, philosophies, or quotations as diamonds to decorate speeches. As the focus of her speech at the 1973 Miss America Pageant, Miss Colorado, Rebecca King, shared her grandmother's philosophy: "The character of a nation is determined by its womanhood." It was perfectly reflective of her style as the first contestant to openly talk of how pageant scholarships were going to help her finance law school, an uncommon aspiration for women at the time. Impressed, the panel awarded her the national title. Her father, Wylie King, later told me that judge Peter Lind Hayes remarked, "She said more in those twenty words than the rest of them did the whole length of time."

Sharing a personal philosophy is great, provided it enhances your image. I remember a Miss Connecticut contestant who delivered this embarrassing New Age ditty:

"I am me. I am a very small part of a large universe. I am intrically [sic] excited. I have a bit of you and everyone else in me. And when all these things are combined, I am—if I can take one bit of pain or discontentment from this world—then I can be very proud to say, 'I am me.'" Every remark you utter onstage should *improve* your image—not spoil it.

Use onstage communication to create a winning image by emphasizing what is special and admirable about you.

93 · Be Prepared for Anything

To communicate to win you've got to be prepared for anything. You can never tell what entry on your fact sheet will catch the emcee's eye and lead to an unusual question, so be prepared for anything and everything. Dick Clark asked one teen contestant to do an impersonation of her favorite character—on live national television. Nothing like a little pressure, but she gamely went along with it.

During one Miss World Pageant, the emcee, noting that Miss Australia had listed astrology on her fact sheet, gave her interview an unexpected twist. "If you had to guess my sign, Miss Australia, what would you say?" While many a contestant would have throttled him for putting them on the spot, the Australian simply studied him for a moment and answered him—correctly. Perhaps she anticipated such a question and checked his birthdate to be on the safe side. At any rate, she turned the unexpected to her advantage.

It never fails that the television host will ask at least one broadcasting major to ad-lib a TV commercial for the pageant. At the 1994 Miss USA Pageant, when Miss Virginia, an aspiring broadcaster, asked TV host Bob Goen, "Can I have your job?" he handed her the mike. She gave such a slick commer-

cial on live TV that she won the interview competition and finished as first runner-up. If you list broadcasting on your
résumé, prepare to "nail" this point-getting opportunity by
practicing television plugs.

One of the "unexpected" things you can expect is being
asked to dabble in a foreign language. This is especially true for
any contestant competing in a contest staged on foreign soil, so
always learn a phrase or two in the host country's tongue. But,
even in pageants on home turf, if you've listed a foreign language on your entry form, be prepared to speak in that language. One young lady who was asked to speak in Swedish—a
common language in her state—so impressed the judges that
they awarded her the Miss USA crown.

Be prepared for anything and make the most of everything!

94 · Sound Like a Winner

Whether it is during a prepared statement, commercial, or
casual conversation with the host, every word you utter
onstage creates an image. Always consider how those words
will make you sound.

Onstage interviews are designed to reveal if a young woman
can think on her feet and articulate her views intelligently.
You've got to be quick-witted to sound like a winner. Consider the national finalist who was asked, "Would you rather be
president of the United States or First Lady?" Read-between-
the-lines translation: Are you a modern woman who knows she
can do anything a man can do, including run a country? Or are
you a prehistoric relic who thinks a wife's place is two steps
behind her husband? This poor dear failed to pick up on the
question's hidden meaning:

"Oh, I think definitely First Lady because I think it is important when you are in a marriage that you really keep your husband in line, so to speak. And I think to keep the president of

the United States in line would be quite an honor, so I definitely would be First Lady."[2]

Hmmm. Being *president* isn't an honor?

Contrast that response with the similar, but more purposeful answer demonstrated by Kenya Moore, who became Miss USA 1993. When asked, "Do you think it is appropriate for a First Lady to participate in her husband's decision-making process as president?" Kenya responded:

"Yes, I think that the First Lady should participate in decision-making for the president. I think that women are always behind their men and a woman has a great influence on her husband or the president, whomever that person may be. A woman has a strong voice and I think it should be heard."[3]

Her predecessor, Shannon Marketic, also demonstrated winning communication when a celebrity judge asked her in front of millions of viewers, "Would you change your mind about voting for a political candidate because of his or her marital infidelity?" As the audience buzzed in acknowledgment of what a "hot potato" the question was, Shannon confidently replied:

"I think that it is important that the elected officials I vote for have private standards as exemplary as their public standards are. I feel that it is important. I feel it is my right and privilege to know that, and I would change my mind if he was practicing infidelity."[4]

Shannon's answer instantly set her apart from the competition and put her on the track to the 1992 Miss USA crown. The ability to express complex thoughts intelligently under pressure makes a woman sound like a winner and instantly sets her apart from entrants who lack that ability.

Never tarnish your image by calling judges' attention to an *unflattering* quality. One national semi-finalist thought she was being cute describing her propensity for accidents—including the time she drove her car onto someone's front porch while they were enjoying breakfast. Another girl joked about her *five* accidents at the pageant, including accidentally hitting three of her fellow contestants and gashing her leg falling down a flight of stairs. Still another contestant gave a blow-by-blow account of her medical problems with anemia, including blood counts. Not exactly the kind of personal tidbits that create a winning image.

Your words are your image. Use them to sound like a winner.

95 · There Are No "Right" or "Wrong" Answers

Although sounding like a winner is absolutely necessary to win, there are no perfect answers guaranteed to impress the judges. What makes an answer successful isn't that it is the "right" answer, but that it is an intelligent answer delivered the right *way*. Say what you think and back it up.

Richard Guy, of the famed GuyRex team that produced five consecutive Miss USAs, describes how radically different equally successful answers can be. When GuyRex staged the 1993 Miss World-America and Miss World-Mexico pageants together, the representatives from both nations were asked, "If the man you are engaged to marry had to move far away and marrying him meant you wouldn't see your family for twenty years, would you marry him? Why or why not?" "The American girl said she would marry the guy because there are so many modern technologies today that she could write and call, and soon there would be a TV where you can see each other on the telephone," recalls Guy. "When I asked the Mexican girl that question, she said, 'Forget it. Another fiancé will come along. You only have one family and I would never leave my family!' They were the same questions," he observes, "but the *thinking* was so different. Yet both were 'correct' answers."

Guy continues: "Another question was, 'You're getting a divorce and you have a son and daughter. By law, you have to give one of them up to the father. Which one would you give up and why?' The American girl said she would not want to give either one of them up, but she would give up the boy because a boy needs a father, and since they are both men, they can relate to each other better. The Mexican girl said that she wouldn't want to give either of them up, but she would give up the daughter because she felt Mexican men were too macho and he would treat the son badly. But women are like little goddesses there and she would give him the daughter because he would treat her wonderfully. They were completely different answers, but both 'correct.'"

As these very different responses demonstrate, there are no right or wrong answers, per se. A winning answer is one that reveals the ability to think on your feet and express your thoughts well under pressure. Onstage interviews "make the girl really think," explains Guy. "You can tell the fake ones, the basic beauty queens who have been programmed, because they can't *think*."

96 · Don't Hide the Obstacles You've Overcome

Sometimes the emcee will ask you to discuss an obstacle you've had to overcome in your life. If you have survived an unusual experience, don't be afraid to share that in a positive manner with the audience and judges. Your background and experiences have made you who you are. If it is a subject that can be discussed on family television, express yourself honestly. During the Miss 1992 Miss World-America Pageant, the eventual winner, Florida's Sharon Beldon, was asked how she had handled growing up as an orphan. She neither sugar-coated her experiences nor manipulated for sympathy votes:

"From a very young age, I had to be very independent and I am a very strong person. I just knew that I had to deal with things and that if I was going to be anything in my life, it was up to me. I am a firm believer that your attitude determines your altitude. I know that I wouldn't be the person that I am today unless I went through what I've been through."[5]

Likewise, Dick Clark asked Miss Teen–Vermont, Charlotte Lopez, a foster child who had lived with six different families over thirteen years, how those experiences had affected her life. She described how she was being adopted as a near-adult and was writing a book, *Lost in the System*, about the failings of the U.S. foster-care system. "It's always easier for me to understand my life if I write it down," she explained, adding "I'm lost in the system and I think there are a lot of kids that are." When she won the 1993 Miss Teen USA title, there wasn't a dry eye in the auditorium.

But isn't that playing on the judges' sympathy? If the young lady deliberately presents it as a sob story, the judges may feel sorry for her but they're not going to see her as the winner. On the other hand, judges expect a young woman to express who she is as an individual. The experiences and hardships of any girl who has survived cancer, a near-fatal accident, the loss of her parents, or being thrust into foster care, are legitimate parts of her life. Sharing that background is merely expressing what she is about as an individual.

If the emcee asks about your life, don't be afraid to mention the experiences that have made you who you are (within good taste; some subjects are too graphic for children who might be watching). Yet, don't *force* that information into the conversation or attempt to manipulate the judges into sympathy votes.

97 · Win With Wit and Humor

When it comes to pageant onstage interviews, humor is a key to the crown. In fact, one of the best indicators of a contestant's chances of winning is her ability to make the judges laugh. The reason is simple. Judges realize that any girl who can be funny, clever, or witty with a celebrity panel and millions of people looking on, has the confidence and sharp mind necessary to be the great titleholder.

Shawn Weatherly turned amusing chitchat into a crown at both the Miss USA and Miss Universe pageants. At Miss USA, host Bob Barker kidded Shawn about what a "trying week" she'd had watching her boyfriend, Dwight Clark, a wide receiver with the San Francisco 49ers, happily snapping pictures of the pretty rivals for the crown. When Shawn joked, "I'm gonna get rid of the negatives," Barker responded mischievously, "He told me he hasn't had film in the camera part of the time." "That's because he's trying to get a little closer to the girls!" Shawn retorted. Humor brought her luck again at the Miss Universe Pageant in Korea, where Barker again kidded her about her flirtatious beau fraternizing with the competition. "He's sitting with my father," Shawn began, gesturing toward a handsome hunk surrounded by dozens of Miss USA contestants who had been flown in as special guests. "I ought to put handcuffs on him so he'll keep his hands off those Miss USA contestants!" she kidded. "Oh, he's with *them?*" replied Barker, playing along. "A happier football player there is not!" The fun dialogue was fresh and enjoyable as compared with many of the duller, more serious conversations.

One of the most memorable uses of humor in a pageant interview was a one-liner dropped by Miss California 1992, Shannon Marketic, in response to the question, "If you were looking for a husband right now, what would you be looking for?" "Well, I would like for him to have mastered the art of monogamy!" Miss California deadpanned as the audience guffawed. "I think that's important—and it's hard to find." When Barker teased, "You mean the guys you are running into are not into that?" Shannon flashed a comically skeptical expression and retorted, "With *Caaaliforniaaaa . . .!?*" Her sharp wit and sense of comedic timing vaulted Shannon from *next-to-last place* going into the semi-finals—to the Miss USA throne.

Win with wit and humor.

98 · *What to Do When You Goof*

There is always the chance for a mistake. It can happen to the most prepared contestant. It can happen to the eventual winner. The bottom line when you've goofed during an onstage interview is: Don't panic!

The way that a young woman handles an onstage flub determines how judges react. If she becomes unsettled by her mistake and loses her composure, the judges will see that she lacks the ability to remain confident and composed under pressure—an absolute requirement for a titleholder. Lose your cool and you lose the crown.

Learn how to recover. One national finalist simply gave up halfway through her answer, removing herself from consideration. When your answer is going in the wrong direction, you've lost your train of thought, or you're "freezing" . . . don't give up. Instead, try these tactics to salvage and *close* your answer:

- Pause and take a breath to compose yourself.
- Keep things simple—focus on *one* train of thought.
- *Restate* what you've just said to close your answer.
- Smile gracefully as if nothing has happened.
- Judges "read" faces so keep your expression *confident*.
- Don't quit. Close.

Responding to a tough question with millions of people watching is a challenge that many eventual winners struggled with. On her way to the 1989 Miss America title, Gretchen Carlson was asked what she thought about the media in the political process. With her background as a Stanford/Oxford honors student who hoped to attend Harvard Law School, the question was a giveaway. Unfortunately, she lost her concentration, heard only part of the question, and gave a mish-mash of Norman Rockwell-ism and legal-speak. "I blew it," she told reporters after her coronation. "I had enough confidence in my intelligence that I thought I could answer the evening gown question to a 'T,' but to be quite frank, when I got offstage, I thought that I had blown it." Luckily for Gretchen, the judges saw past the glitch to her bright mind and awarded her the national title.

As Carlson's experience demonstrates, *you* may think your gaffe has cost you the crown, but, in reality, the judges may overlook a mistake and score you highly for other interview qualities such as personality and poise. It ain't over until that crown's on somebody's head, so don't let a mistake undermine your confidence and composure.

99 · Clinch the Crown With the Final Question!

It's anybody's crown—until the final question clinches the title for one lucky girl. As former Miss Universe and pageant co-anchor Margaret Gardener put it as she watched several Miss Universe finalists head for the isolation booth, "They may *look* calm, cool and collected, but they are in absolute turmoil. They realize that this reply can change their futures. It is the very best—and worst—moment of their entire life."

The final question, ultimately, is a test of composure that distinguishes the young woman who is most qualified to serve as the titleholder. The contestant demonstrating the most confidence and ability to express herself under pressure simply comes across to judges as the woman who would best fulfill the job. The onstage questions are so important that fabulous answers have yanked several finalists with previously mediocre standings to the throne. In 1992, Shannon Marketic entered the Miss USA top ten in ninth place, and then scored only sixth in gown and swimsuit. After barely squeezing into the finals, she wowed the judges with her great communication skills and walked off with the Miss USA crown. Arkansas' Teri Utley slipped into the top twelve in eleventh place, went into the final question in third place, and performed well enough to earn the 1982 Miss USA crown. During the 1992 Miss Universe Pageant, Miss Namibia, who was fourth in the finals, performed so superbly during the final question that she clinched the crown.

(MISS UNIVERSE, INC.)

The final question is often where the crown is won or lost. Above, Miss Venezuela, TV host Bob Goen—and the famous isolation booth. She placed as first runner-up to Miss Universe 1994.

The crown rests on your being poised and professional under pressure. Maintaining composure during the enormous pressures of answering a final question with as many as 600 million viewers watching reveals that a young lady has the confidence to fulfill the responsibilities of the crown.

For example, during the 1981 Miss Universe Pageant Bob Barker asked the five finalists, "If the Miss Universe Pageant could offer you the right to have one wish come true—*not* for the world—but for you personally, what would it be?" Four of the five finalists made blunders, including the eventual winner, Miss Venezuela, Irene Saez. Despite the interpreter translating Bob's instructions, Saez replied, "To achieve peace in the world." Startled, Barker repeated that it *not* be for the world. Despite the rocky beginning, Irene maintained her composure, calmly nodded her understanding of the host's correction, and recovered with a diplomatic answer that outclassed the other finalists. Remaining regal in the heat of the spotlight clinched the Miss Universe crown for her.

Even after an entire week of competition, communicating to win during a final question can change the direction of the crown. During the 1992 Miss America Pageant, before Regis Philbin asked each of the five finalists a final question about her platform, the celebrity judges were still unsure which young woman would win. But by the time Miss Florida, Leanza Cornett, finished discussing her AIDS prevention and education platform, the judges were convinced she should hold the national title. Soon after Cornett's victory, a British pageant fan wrote to tell me that the conviction and sincerity of Leanza's final answer had so moved him, that when she was crowned he stood in the privacy of his home and *saluted* her. Now that's communicating to win.

The final question is a test of each finalists' total suitability for the title. Judges are adding the final touches to their judging by asking themselves: Which woman *overall* is most qualified to wear the crown? It is a young woman's best—and last—opportunity to clinch the crown.

There is no question that a winner knows how to communicate to win. Whether you are asked to deliver a prepared statement, chat with the master of ceremonies, or answer a judge's question extemporaneously, your comments should reflect the intelligence, personality, and confidence expected of a titleholder. Use onstage communication as a key to the crown.

NINE

Your Final Steps in Pursuit of the Crown . . .

Never give up.
Never. Never. Never. Never.
WINSTON CHURCHILL

You've worked and improved . . . prepared and practiced . . . entered and competed . . . and *lost*. The crown still remains out of grasp. What next? Enter again? Give up?

100 · If You Can't Win . . . Change States

You do not have to accept losing as inevitable. Many contestants who lost and lost and lost at the state level, found that their solution was simple: *Change states*. In fact, state-shopping is a common practice today among girls who can't seem to break the barrier to their home state's throne. "There are two choices," explains Mary Donnelly-Haskell, a former Miss Mississippi who won her home state's crown on the first try. "She can stay and say, 'I'm going to prove them wrong. I can win this pageant.' Or she can say, 'Maybe it's not in the cards here . . . maybe this isn't the location for me,' and move to another state. There's no denying the fact that it's worked for several girls, some who have even gone on to win the [national] crown." Since a contestant who could only make the top ten in a tough state pageant might *win* in a less competitive one, changing states can boost an entrant's chances of victory.

Consider Debra Maffett, the most famous example of the switch-to-win strategy. Maffett, a resident of tiny Cut 'n Shoot, Texas, couldn't manage to nab the state title. Realizing that there wasn't a crown in her future in the Lone Star state, and with her twenty-fifth birthday sneaking up, Debbie decided to change strategies. Instead of wasting precious time trying for Miss Texas again, she moved to California, worked on improving her appearance, won the Miss Anaheim and Miss California titles, and became Miss America 1983. Debbie's decision to switch to win paid off in royal rhinestones!

Changing states is permitted in most systems as long as entrants meet residency rules—usually by living, working, or attending classes full-time in the new state for six months before the local contest.

Many such contestants move from tough states in the South, where as many as sixty entrants battle for a state title, to less-competitive states in the West, Northwest, or New England, where as few as eight contestants compete. States worth considering include: Alaska, Oregon, Washington, Montana, Wyoming, Nebraska, South Dakota, North Dakota, Colorado, Nevada, New Mexico, Arizona, Idaho, Delaware, Maryland, Vermont, Maine, Rhode Island, New Hampshire, Massachusetts, and Connecticut.

Girls who are residents of one state, but attend college in another, are usually eligible to compete in either state. Sylvia Hitchcock, a Floridian, was chosen Miss USA and Miss Universe while a student in Alabama. Miss America 1990, Debbye Turner, lost Miss Arkansas several times but later won Miss Missouri while attending veterinary school there. Rebecca King, of Iowa, won the Miss Colorado title while entering law school there and became Miss America 1974. If you have a choice of two states, enter the pageant with less competition.

An entrant's decision can have major repercussions. I remember one gorgeous young woman who entered a pageant in her very competitive home state for years, always finishing as a runner-up. During her final year of eligibility, she decided to compete in her state one last time. Sadly, she lost (to a girl who had moved there after losing in Mississippi!). Because she decided not to try her luck elsewhere, this superb contestant—who was qualified to compete on the national level—never won even a state title. Sometimes, knowing when to try your luck elsewhere can be the most important decision you can make.

Yet changing states is no guarantee. Another girl who finished as first runner-up in her state, moved to Virginia—where she failed to make the top five. "I think the fact that I had been in the state for only a few months prior to winning my local hurt my chances," she told me anonymously. "There was some bad press. Rumors and bad gossip spread around. I think it caught up with the judges. In a way, I was poisoned."

Another problem with state-hopping is that when it is done blatantly it can lead to nasty scandals. One year, a Pennsylvania girl won the Miss New Jersey title after she enrolled at a college there, but never attended classes. She was challenged in court by her runner-up, a bona fide resident of New Jersey. Although the judge allowed the winner to keep the title, her week at the nationals was ruined when tabloids rehashed the scandal and spectators booed her. While switching states is worth considering for a serious contestant who just can't seem to win her state title, it must be handled impeccably to avoid unpleasant publicity or court challenges. Find out the exact residency requirements and meet them to the letter.

Also, out of courtesy to the people you will represent if you win, get to know your adopted state. Represent them with sincerity and pride.

101 · Let Failure Prepare You to Win

"Never give up. Never. Never. Never. Never." Winston Churchill's famous words should be engraved on every entry form in the pageant world, for it is the singular quality that distinguishes winners from losers in pageants . . . and life.

The importance of never giving up is underscored by the fact that, of the last twenty-five Miss Americas, eighteen suffered losses prior to victory. Several competed for half a decade before winning. If you've lost and the crown appears forever out of reach, be encouraged . . . the road to the throne is usually paved with losses.

Cheryl Prewitt's road to the national runway took half a decade. "Everybody thinks that Miss Americas have always won," she says, chuckling. "Boy are they wrong! I went in every year for five years—and lost. I finally won my first local pageant after four years." Finally, in her fifth year, her elusive dream became reality when she was crowned Miss Mississippi and Miss America 1980. "I worked five years for the dream that God put in my heart. I could have given up after that many years because it was beginning to be embarrassing, but I decided to stick it out. And it paid off."

Although grueling, Cheryl's years of "failure" transformed her into a champion. "I can honestly say that I learned more about myself and I improved more the years that I lost, rather than the year that I won," she says, "because losing is a learning process. The only time I actually improve is when I'm following myself, when I'm going against the grain, which is what losing is. That's what takes me from the rough stone to a polished diamond."

Similarly, Kaye Lani Rae Rafko lost for six years before finally winning the triple crown. She narrowly lost at Miss Michigan several times, failed to make the top ten at Miss Ohio, and then suffered through a dry spell when she couldn't win a local title. She nearly quit. But after she opened a fortune cookie that predicted, "Your dreams will come true next year," her father and fiancé encouraged her to give it one more try. She took their advice, won her coveted national title . . . and became one of the all-time greats in pageantry.

Throughout Kaye Lani's six years of losing she continued to reenter and improve, reenter and improve, trusting that God has purposes for every experience—even "failures." "I really think God had a reason for having me keep working at my goal," she says. "After six-and-a-half years I would have a message to give to others. My message was that with determination and hard work I was able to achieve goals and go much farther than I could have possibly imagined. . . ."

Another inspirational success story is Dr. Debbye Turner, whose arduous road to the 1990 Miss America crown would have exhausted a lesser competitor. Like Kaye Lani and Cheryl, she attributes her success to a stubborn refusal to give up. "In my own life, determination and hard work and tenacity have been the keys to success," says Turner. "It took me seven years and eleven tries in two states to get here . . . and I'm so glad I didn't stop trying! What is important is that with each failure we learn what else it takes to succeed and that we never give up."

In fact, failure is often a catalyst for success, inspiring the perseverance and steady improvement that transform a contestant into a champion. Debra Maffett is a perfect example. Her five years of losing actually equipped her to serve as a national titleholder. She says:

"As I look back on it, the whole experience was a growth process. I shouldn't have won before because mentally I wasn't ready, my talent wasn't ready, and I wasn't ready for the [national] stage. And I don't think I could have handled the job. I was just a slow starter. But, by the time I won, I was ready. I was capable of handling the job and of doing a good job with it. So, it's fortunate I *didn't* win before."

As these outstanding women prove, winners are often the individuals whose roads to the crown are the most difficult. Their failures shape them for victory and their perseverance literally carves a pathway to the throne. As Dr. Debbye Turner advises, no matter what setbacks you must overcome in pursuit of the crown, "Do exactly what it is that you dream of doing—because I am living proof that dreams really come true."

Never give up. And never lose sight of your dream.

Conclusion

Only one girl can win the crown. But any girl who enters
pageants with a spirit of competition and a desire to better
herself through that competition will always be a winner
in the eyes of those who love her.
　　　　MARY DONNELLY-HASKELL, FORMER MISS MISSISSIPPI

The first step in turning your dreams into reality is understanding that famous titles are won by real people. Real
girls grow up to be Miss World, Miss USA, and Miss Universe.
And, quite frankly, most of the time, not a soul around them
ever suspected that that little girl next door would one day
walk down a runway on live television wearing one of the most
coveted crowns in the world. But dreams do come true. Many
of you reading this book *will* become Miss America, Miss USA,
America's Junior Miss, and Miss Teen USA. Some of you will
step into Cinderella's slippers and wear the crown before the
year is out.

I had a front-row view of one such modern-day Cinderella
story in 1992 when I judged the Miss America Pageant. One of
our contestants that year, Leanza Cornett, was just another
attractive college student with big dreams . . . perhaps like
you. During the national judges' interviews I came face-to-face

with Leanza. She was great—confident, articulate, pretty, and perfectly groomed. But, frankly, I couldn't have predicted at that moment that she would walk away with the crown. By the conclusion of the fifty interviews, our panel was still uncertain who would emerge as our winner. Yet, by the end of a week of onstage competitions, Cornett had performed so superbly that, when the points were tabulated she had earned the national crown. In the months that followed, Leanza became such a successful titleholder that she was offered a starring role on Broadway and a coveted four-year cohosting contract with "Entertainment Tonight." (She passed on Broadway and signed with "E.T."). Leanza's dream vaulted her from obscurity to a glamorous, high-visibility position other people work a lifetime to achieve. Leanza not only made her dream a reality. She surpassed it.

Leanza's example illustrates that a winner makes herself a winner, whether or not those around her realize that she has what it takes to achieve such success. The crown—any crown—is earned by those young women who dare to believe in themselves and to invest in their dreams.

If you decide to invest in your dreams by pursuing the crown, undertake that challenge with the commitment to excellence expected of an aspiring champion. As one Miss USA who spoke anonymously put it: "Realize that it's a competition. I've never heard of an athlete who is going to the Olympics say that they're going there to have fun. They're going there to win the gold medal! If you can enjoy yourself *and* win the gold medal at the same time, that's great—but it's still a competition. And *pageants* are a competition."

Always give your best when you compete, but keep in mind that, like the Olympics, only one individual can win the ultimate prize. No one would dream of looking down upon an individual who missed the Olympic gold medal but won the bronze, or who made the American Olympic team, or set a state record in an Olympic sport. In the same manner, not bringing home a national, state, or local title in no way diminishes the value of what you *do* accomplish as you compete.

Every competitor must participate with realistic expectations and be prepared to accept whatever outcome with a positive perspective. As Debra Maffett advises from experience, the ultimate purpose for competing is to build a life of success and purpose. "Never consider [winning] as an end in itself," she cautions. "Know that there is a huge element of luck. The very worst that can happen through pursuing this dream is that you become a better human being. There is life after pageants. Know who you are and what your visions and dreams are," she advises confidently, "because you'll get them."

You never can tell where the road to the crown may lead you. So go ahead—apply the principles of this book, give your best effort, fight for the crown, refuse to be discouraged by failure, and enter again and again in pursuit of your dream. Because, within the next few years, a dozen or so of you reading this book will become Miss Universe, Miss America, or Miss USA. Hundreds of you will hold state titles. Perhaps thousands of you will become proud local titleholders. Every one of these accomplishments is an honor. Like the contestants who walked the runway before you, you are a true winner for daring to step out of the audience to pursue success.

My hope as the author is that, as you pursue the crown, *101 Secrets to Winning Beauty Pageants* will provide you with the keys to achieve your dreams. Perhaps one day I will have the pleasure of watching you glide down the runway victoriously. Until that wonderful moment, here's to your quest for the crown . . . .

Notes

Chapter 3: The Winning "Package"

1. Dr. Lillian Glass, *Talk to Win!*

2. Ibid.

3. "Miss America Born Beautiful? Not Necessarily," *Sunday Republican*, September 13, 1992, p. TV-3. Springfield, Massachusetts.

4. Jay Reeves, "Breast Implant Makers to Pay $4.25 Billion," *Union-News*, September 2, 1994, p.1. Springfield, Massachusetts.

5. Ibid.

6. Liz Hunt, "Risk of Breast Implants Made Public," *Union-News*, October 5, 1991, p. 18; reprinted from the *Washington Post*.

7. Jill Stein, "Breast Implants Conceal Cancer," *Reader's Digest*, p. 64; November 1987, reprinted from *Oncology Times*.

8. "Cosmetic Surgery Botched," *Miami Herald*, April 5, 1989, p. 10A.

9. Donald Robinson, "The Truth About Cosmetic Surgery," *Reader's Digest*, February 1991, pp. 75–80

Chapter 4: The Winning Interview

1. Lisa DePaulo, "Miss America—Was Last Year's Voting Suspect?," *TV Guide*, September 2, 1989.
2. Dream Girl USA Pageant telecast ©, 1987.

Chapter 5: The Winning Swimsuit

1. Frank H. Mahnke, *Color and Light in Man-Made Environments* (New York: Van Nostrand Reinhold Company, 1987), p.17.
2. Ibid.
3. Katy Koontz, "The Power of Color," *New Woman* April 1992, p. 72–74.
4. Tim Friend, "Indoor Tan Puts 'Stress' on the Body" *USA Today*, September 16, 1988.

Chapter 7: The Winning Evening Gown

1. Katy Koontz, "The Power of Color," *New Woman*, April 1992, p. 73.
2. Ibid.
3. Deborah T. Sharpe, *The Psychology of Color and Design* (Chicago: Nelson-Hall Co., 1974).
4. James Gray, Jr., *The Winning Image*, (New York: Anacom, 1982), pp. 67–69.
5. Maryl Cundiff, "Body Language: The Power Behind the Words," *The Toastmaster*, April 1978, pp. 17–19.

Chapter 8: Winning Onstage Communication

1. 1987 Miss America Pageant telecast ©, September 1987.
2. Miss USA Pageant telecast ©, February 1992.
3. 1993 Miss USA Pageant telecast ©, February 1993.
4. 1992 Miss USA Pageant telecast ©, February 1992.
5. Miss 1992 World-America Pageant telecast ©, August 1992.

Index

Index